For the first time ever, the gimlet eye of a tiny literary colossus – small in stature but mighty in influence – unlocks the closely guarded secrets of the British monarchy. How? Because he's one of them.

Clare worked extremely hard in film, television and on charity campaigns before becoming a full-time writer. This included romantic comedies such as *Love Actually* and *Bridget Jones's Diary*, Comic Relief, Make Poverty History and Live 8, and the BBC's *Planet Word* with Stephen Fry. She was Commissioning Editor at *Tatler* magazine and is now a Contributing Editor. She lives in west London.

The Prince George Diaries

CLARE BENNETT

MICHAEL JOSEPH

an imprint of

PENGUIN BOOKS

MICHAEL JOSEPH

UK | USA | Canada | Ireland | Australia
India | New Zealand | South Africa

Michael Joseph is part of the Penguin Random House group of companies
whose addresses can be found at global.penguinrandomhouse.com.

First published 2015
001

Set in 11.75/16.25 pt Simoncini Garamond Std
Typeset by Jouve (UK), Milton Keynes
Printed in Great Britain by Clays Ltd, St Ives plc

A CIP catalogue record for this book is available from the British Library

ISBN: 978–0–718–18253–3

www.greenpenguin.co.uk

Penguin Random House is committed to a
sustainable future for our business, our readers
and our planet. This book is made from Forest
Stewardship Council® certified paper.

For Mum and Dad

Let us not take ourselves too seriously.

Queen Elizabeth II

July 2014

22nd July 2014

Today I woke to discover my entire team in my room. Usually it's just my choir singing 'Land of Hope and Glory', but this morning they were singing something else. A song called 'Happy Birthday'. Even Mummy and Daddy were there, joining in with the harmonies and beaming over my cot.

'Today is a special day, Georgie,' Mummy said to me. 'You are a year old.'

'That's right – happy birthday!' Daddy said.

'Id est rectus – felicem natalem diem!' repeated my Latin teacher.

The whole room gave me a round of applause.

'Birthdays are very special,' Mummy said. 'People like to make a fuss of you and spoil you and give you presents. Like a normal day, but better.'

My Press Secretary stepped forward.

'If I may, Sir, you'll be pleased to hear that, so far, the birthday photo campaign we shot at the Natural

History Museum three weeks ago is being received exceptionally well. Beyond our expectations.'

'The stripy-dungarees-and-navy-polo-shirt approach we opted for is crashing the internet for copycat looks as we speak,' said my stylist.

'And thanks to the staged interaction with the Blue Morpho, where you pretended to try and grab its wings,' loud laughter from everyone, 'we've successfully highlighted the importance and delight of butterflies,' said my Zoologist.

'We feel strongly that the look we were going for has been successful,' continued my Mood Analyst. 'Whimsical, fascinated, deep in thought – like you're composing a poem or considering the laws of the universe.'

'They love the hair,' said my Hairdresser.

'And they love the walking,' said my Walking Coach.

'Basically, Sir,' said my head of Global Strategy, 'you've smashed it again.'

I bounced in my cot a bit. Kicked that toy bilby Australia gave me.

Another round of applause.

After breakfast, I had a meeting with my Present Team. From what I gather, not everyone gets presents every day. They are generally given on things called 'special occasions', which means something needs to have happened for you to get one. Just being yourself, you know, on a Tuesday or something, isn't enough.

Odd – because I've been given around four thousand

presents in the past 365 days, which averages just under eleven a day.

The Present Team gave me a tour of what I'd received and I was pleased because I got some cool things. There was a handmade rocking horse from my friends the Obamas, with the presidential seal on the saddle, which is nice, and then more of the usual – clothes, toys, games, rare breeds of animal.

I wonder what the fattened bull is doing today, the one the people of Samburu in Kenya gave me when I was born. I think it came with some kind of goat, but I'm not 100 per cent sure. Sometimes I think about those meerkats that were named after me too. Meerkats can eat scorpions. I bet their nannies don't make *them* eat kale (take a good look at yourself, Maria Teresa).

What I was mostly hoping, though, was that they would let me see that crocodile I was given by Darwin. He is also called George. He was hatched the day Mummy and Daddy said I was going to be born, so he's kind of like a brother to me. A brother I have never met who is in no way heir to the throne, just to clear that up! *Looks around nervously.* LOL.

We decided to give my new presidential horse a whirl, so Mummy held me in the saddle and we rode for a bit.

I pulled its mane and shouted and Daddy took pictures of me on the iPad. Or, at least, he tried to.

'Babykins, how does this thing work again? Why is it taking pictures of me? I don't understand . . .'

I shouted again and made a grabbing motion at it.

'It's not unequivocally an anxiety-related demand, but I think there is pending frustration there,' my Movement Interpreter said quietly to Mummy.

'Give it to George,' Mummy said to Daddy. 'He hasn't started his digital-equipment course yet, but he'll probably understand it.'

Daddy was scratching his head and turning the iPad round and round. I grabbed it from him and immediately pressed the reverse camera symbol and then pressed the big round button at the bottom, taking a picture of the floor. I mean, LOLZ out loud, this is not complicated stuff.

Mummy smirked, pointing at Daddy, and said, 'Thicky.'

'He's so clever,' Daddy said. 'Takes after his mother.' Then he laughed a bit and his cheeks went pink.

'What's happened here is that George has immediately tapped into the principle of the iPad, which is based on instinct,' my Movement Interpreter said quietly, 'and he has demonstrated this skill by taking a photo of the floor.'

'Have that framed, please,' Mummy said.

There was a knock at the door.

'Come on, Georgie,' Mummy said, picking me up. 'Let's go and talk birthday outfits.'

We were taken through a presentation by my stylist and Wardrobe Team, who showed us the various options they'd picked out for me. I didn't make a public appearance today, but Mummy still wanted something special, so we opted for the Royal Guardsman outfit.

'This is a good choice for phase one,' said my stylist. 'It's from the Royal Collection Trust, so it's strategically strong for your visit to HQ this morning. And if we do decide to leak the story, it'll be good for revenue.'

'Granny will like that,' Daddy said, out of the corner of his mouth to Mummy.

'Anything that makes your great-grandmother, GG, happy makes us happy, doesn't it, George?' Mummy said to me. 'Let's go for it.'

When I'd got changed, we went to HQ to see G-Pop because he couldn't come to my party. Sad face :(

G-Pop is the oldest human on earth. His first pet was a dinosaur and he invented fire. He didn't learn to stand up straight or communicate using language until he was twenty-five and he still eats with his hands when he's on his own. I know all this because Uncle Harry told me.

When we got to HQ, G-Pop was sitting in his chair with a blanket over his knees and Mummy put me on his lap.

'What the bloody hell is he wearing?' G-Pop bellowed at Mummy and Daddy. 'He looks completely deranged.'

'It's a guardsman outfit,' Daddy said nervously. 'It's meant to be sort of sweet and funny.'

'I'll tell you what's funny. Stoke-on-Trent, that's what. If you find things that are totally ghastly *funny*,' G-Pop said.

'George is one today,' Mummy said calmly. 'We brought him here so you could wish him a happy birthday.'

'Doesn't say much, does he?' G-Pop grumbled.

'He can't talk yet,' Daddy said, 'because he's only one.'

'I'd shot a rhino and been appointed first lieutenant of HMS *Whelp* by the time I was one,' G-Pop said crossly.

Mummy and Daddy looked at each other.

'Well, as good as,' G-Pop said again, waving his hand around.

He turned to me.

'It's no good sitting there like a sack of ferrets – a man's got to speak up for himself. Otherwise he gets pushed around and expected to fanny about on a tour of French Polynesia wearing a grass skirt and eating seahorses when all he wants is a plate of barbecued sausages in front of the cricket.'

'Is that the time? Gosh, we have to go,' Mummy said, picking me up. 'It's been so lovely to see you.'

'When are you going to cut that ridiculous hair?' G-Pop said to Mummy. 'Makes you look like a guinea pig. Can't tell which end is which.'

Mummy and Daddy were almost sort of running out of the door by then, but I made sure I waved to G-Pop over their shoulders. It looked like he was shaking his fist at me, but I couldn't be sure. G-Pop is such a hoot.

We had my birthday party at home in the afternoon and, I must say, I thoroughly enjoyed myself. Aunt P and Uncle J organized it for me because they are so good at parties they do it as an actual job. Aunt P even wrote a whole book about it once.

I was excited to see my godparents, but they seemed to be behaving a bit weirdly. They were staring at each other's presents and I heard one of them saying, 'Christ, I only got him a jigsaw. "Guess who" has bought him twenty-four bottles of Dow's Vintage '63.'

(By the way, what *is* port and why does it have to lie down for so long?)

There was this funny moment when everyone stood up and that was when GG arrived. She gave me something made of china and I'm not allowed to play with it because Mummy says it is from the Royal Collection and it's very valuable. They won't let me throw it, so I'm not sure what the point of it is. I just have to look at it on a shelf, they said.

GG spent some time talking to Grandpa M, who was dressed as a large bumblebee. He loves fancy dress *so much*. At my christening, he got changed into a hot-dog outfit straight after the photos. I think it's cheerful, but Granny C never seems to like his costumes.

'I just don't know about this outfit, Mike. I mean, this is the Queen we're talking about,' I heard her say quietly.

'Well, not for a while yet,' Grandpa M replied, and Granny C frowned, saying, 'Don't be facetious – you know I'm not talking about Squeak,' looking at Mummy. 'I mean the *actual . . .*' They both looked at GG.

'Excuse me, have you seen what she has to wear to the State Opening of Parliament? No one knows better about fancy dress than Her Majesty. Why do you think we get on so well?' Grandpa M said.

After that Granny C sort of had to agree. GG does wear fancy dress a lot. The capes are good, but she always says she prefers the Order of the Garter hat to the Imperial State Crown, because that 'weighs a ton and wobbles like a drunk on an ice rink'.

Uncle Harry was a bit late and he came running through the door, beating his chest and shouting, 'ME WANT CAKE!'

First he high-fived Mummy and they did the funny hand-clapping rhyme, which they always do, that no one else understands, and then he got Daddy in a head-lock, which he also always does and Daddy went a bit red and laughed in a strange high voice, saying, 'Um, I'm sort of suffocating, Spike,' and Harry just laughed and rubbed his knuckle into the top of Daddy's head, saying, 'Wombat, darling! It's been two days – I missed you.'

And Daddy quietly said, 'Ow,' like he always does and then Uncle Harry just pushed him onto the floor, got him in a stranglehold and made Daddy beg for mercy.

He only let him go when GG said, 'Thank you, Harry, but I think we'd all prefer it if William was able to spend George's birthday fully conscious.'

And then Uncle Harry dropped him and bounded up to her, giving her a big kiss on the cheek, saying, 'Excellent plan, Lilibet,' and GG rolled her eyes and smacked him on the arm with a napkin that used to belong to Queen Victoria.

Uncle Harry is always in a good mood. He shouted, 'Happy birthday, Small G, you absolute legend!' when he saw me and then he let me ride around on his back before we unwrapped the special birthday present he got me.

'It's a shrunken head,' he said brightly. 'A Jivaroan tribe in South America gave it to me and now I want you to have it. I think it's one of the old British ambassadors in Ecuador, but I can't be certain.'

It looked like a sort of coconut with teeth, so I rolled it around a bit.

GG peered over at it. 'I didn't know we'd invited the Duke of Kent,' she said.

When it was time for my birthday cake, Uncle Harry suggested quietly to me that I should just grab a big old handful of it when it was brought in and shove it straight in my mouth, like a Viking would, so I did. Everyone had been singing that song from this morning and Daddy was still all flustered, trying to take a photo on the iPad again.

'Rats, I missed it. I just can't . . . Babykins, this is so complicated, I don't . . .'

It was fine, though, because they simply brought in another cake, which looked exactly the same and I heard the chef say to Mummy, 'Don't worry, Ma'am, we'd always planned for a back-up. We have several spares in waiting.'

'Story of our lives . . .' Uncle Harry said.

Most of the people at my party were grown-ups, but Cousin Mia came along as well. It's quite hard for me to play with her because she's only seven months and I am one, which is a lot older. Uncle Harry said the best way to jolly things along would be if I gave her some crisps, but 'not by handing her some – make it more fun. Like it's raining crisps.' Uncle Harry gets on with everyone, so I took his advice and threw them at her head, but she started crying because she's a girl.

I don't really understand girls, to be quite honest. Uncle Harry says he doesn't either. When she tried to play with one of my trucks, I took it off her so I could show her how to ram it into a wall. But then it stopped working.

Normally Mummy would call the Toy-fixing Team when that happens, but because GG was there, we didn't have to. She always has a set of tiny tools in her handbag and she fixes all my cars if they break. She put on her glasses, turned my truck upside down and fiddled around with it a bit, muttering, 'Looks like a problem with the chassis . . .' and five minutes later it was working again. One day I'll get her to teach me how to change a spark plug and that will eventually make me the second monarch ever who knows how to do that.

Anyway, we played some brilliant games, which Aunt P organised.

We started off with Pin the Tail on the Cheltenham Gold Cup Winner (GG won that – she was *so* happy). Then it was Pass the Castle (whoever unwraps the key when the music ends wins a castle – GG won that again and said, 'Wait, I thought I already owned this one?') and Musical Heirs (Uncle J won that and everyone looked confused). Then GG had to go home, so the party was over.

I'm so tired now. But this has been a good day. I hope it's my birthday tomorrow too. Mummy was right – birthdays are even better than normal days.

23rd July

Woke up excited at the thought that this would be another birthday, but apparently it was just a normal day. No cake, no party, no nothing. Apart from the usual haul of presents from around the world, but obviously that doesn't count.

I'm not going to lie. This did not go down well. These people have gone back to expecting me to eat spinach instead of just cake and I'm pretty outraged. Mental note to self: make every day a birthday when in the Top Job. GG has got the ball rolling with two and, quite frankly, why stop there?

We went swimming at HQ today and then I went and hung around with GG while she was having her chat with David, who must be her best friend because they see each other every week. They usually get served tea when he comes and David always says he won't have any sandwiches, but then he changes his mind. It was the same today.

'Maybe just one,' David said.

'Jam or smoked salmon, Prime Minister?' GG said.

'It's so hard to decide,' David said. 'Maybe I'll have one jam and one smoked salmon?'

'Good idea,' GG said.

'My party and I are committed to fairness after all!'

He laughed very loudly.

'Indeed,' GG said.

David then seemed to have already finished both the sandwiches.

'Small, aren't they,' he said.

'Perhaps it's because they've had the crusts taken off,' GG suggested.

David eyed the cake.

'Do you ever get those mid-afternoon cravings?' he asked.

'When one is busy, it's inevitable,' GG said. 'And I was brought up always to have tea.'

'Yes, so was I, so was I,' David said, looking very serious. 'That must be why I'm always so starving around now. Although it shouldn't happen because my diet is very balanced, which is how I stay so trim. And because I don't tend to go for the chocolatey things if there's a choice, but I might make an exception today.'

He then ate most of the cake, looking quite guilty.

It usually takes her a while, but GG then makes them talk about other things to do with David's job. I prefer to go through GG's handbag, which she always lets me play with. I can never open the silver case she keeps her mini tools in, but I had a hoot drawing on the walls with her lipstick – I did it behind the curtain and no one seems to have noticed yet, LOL. She also usually carries some chocs for the Mean Girls, as Uncle Harry has nicknamed GG's dogs, which taste pretty weird, but who cares, they still count as chocolate. And then there's this funny little stone that she keeps in the pocket with the zip. I roll it around sometimes, but I don't know what it's for. Sometimes she just holds it in her hand and looks at it and then she puts it back again.

Holly and Willow absolutely lost it the last time I ate their dog chocs and had to be removed from the room by GG's Private Secretary. Apparently they've become even more impossible since they were in that James Bond film for the Olympics. Daddy says it really went to their heads. The Dorgis are just as bad. People said Great Great Aunt Margaret had an attitude you could carbon offset, but this lot are next level.

26th July

Mummy and Daddy are going to the Commonwealth Games in Scotland with Uncle Harry tomorrow. Earlier this week Mummy said that she was nervous the hockey team were going to make her join in, like they did before the Olympics. She says she used to be captain of the hockey team at school, but that was a long time ago.

We kept finding her running along the corridors at home with a hockey stick, dribbling a ball between the furniture, so Daddy had a mock pitch set up in our garden so she could practise taking penalty corners.

'It came back to me during the Olympics,' I heard her telling Daddy, 'but that was two years ago and I've had George since then. I'm just not as fast as I used to be.'

'You'll be so marvellous, though, Babykins,' Daddy said. 'And if you're feeling rusty, well, that's OK too.'

'Do you really think so?' Mummy asked anxiously.

'Why don't we have a little practice and if you're feeling insecure, we'll get the Olympic hockey coach in to bring you up to speed again,' Daddy said.

'I suppose so . . .' Mummy said, biting her lip.

'OK, well, I'll stand in goal and we'll just go slowly,' Daddy said, patting her on the shoulder. 'Maybe just informally play around a bit. Help you get used to it all again. Does that sound OK?'

Mummy nodded and took a few paces back.

Daddy got into goal and Mummy took a deep breath. 'I wonder if I've still got it,' she said quietly, before suddenly whacking the ball. It shot up into the air, flying in a perfect arc right over Daddy's shoulder into the back of the net. Mummy leant casually on her hockey stick and winked at Daddy. 'Oh, look – it turns out I do.' She smirked, breezily dropping her stick and picking me up to go back inside. Daddy just stood there speechless.

'Remember, Georgie,' she said to me, 'it's important to be brilliant at absolutely everything, like Mummy is, but that doesn't mean you should let on straight away. Keep them guessing. Take them by surprise.'

'She totally played me, George,' Daddy said later, shaking his head. 'How could I have fallen for that when I know she's basically a supreme being who could probably, you know, reverse time or make milk rise from the earth?' He stared at her. 'She takes my breath away,' he added dreamily.

27th July

Mummy, Daddy and Uncle Harry are in Scotland and they Skyped me after supper. Daddy said watching the hockey was fun, but it would have been even better if Mummy had been playing because she is the best player in the entire universe. Mummy said that was probably true – and then Uncle Harry appeared in the background, waving an enormous drink about, and shouted, 'Ah, Small G – slainte mhath!' and then he and Mummy had a conversation in their secret language and Daddy couldn't join in because they won't explain it to him.

Instead, Daddy held up a big yellow kangaroo, which had large red boxing gloves on, and waved it at me. 'This is a present for you from the Australian swimming team,' he explained. 'Isn't that nice of them?'

'Is it just me or does that thing have eyes exactly like Russell Crowe?' Uncle Harry said, taking the kangaroo from Daddy. He held it up in front of his face. 'My name is Maximus Decimus Macropodidae, commander of the Armies of the Northern Territory, general of the Marsupial Legions, loyal servant to the *true* queen, Elizabeth II.' He handed it to Mummy.

'Father to a murdered joey, husband to a murdered possum. And I will have my vengeance, in this semi-arid billabong or the next,' she made it say, in a deep, dramatic voice.

Then they were both having hysterics and Uncle Harry took it again.

'Are you not entertained?? *ARE YOU NOT ENTERTAINED??*'

Then Daddy took it and sang something about someone called Jean Valjean and the number 24601.

Mummy and Uncle Harry stopped laughing and looked confused.

'You know – the bit when Anne Hathaway has just died and Russell Crowe tries to arrest Hugh Jackman,' Daddy said.

'That's *Les Mis*,' Mummy said.

'We're quoting from *Gladiator*, darling,' Uncle Harry said, 'which, on reflection, I cannot *believe* they didn't make into a musical. What a missed opportunity.'

And then he and Mummy fell about laughing and Daddy's cheeks went a bit pink and he said, 'Right, right. I love *Gladiator*, actually. I know it very well,' and then Uncle Harry grabbed him round the neck to make him feel better and they disappeared out of shot onto the floor with a great crash while Mummy shouted, 'At my bouncing, unleash hell!'

I was quite jealous not to be there, actually.

30th July

Mummy, Daddy and Uncle Harry are back from the Commonwealth Games. They said that yesterday they hung around with their friend Usain Bolt, who Uncle Harry named his horse 'Usain Colt' after.

Mummy was going through her schedule for the week. Uncle Harry and Daddy were meant to be practising some speeches they're both due to give, but they kept standing up and doing lightning-bolt poses instead.

'I raced him in Jamaica, of course,' Uncle Harry was saying. 'I mean, he was fast, yes, but I wasn't really trying. I kind of let him let me win, if you know what I mean.'

'This feels really cool,' Daddy said, increasing his lunge. 'I *feel* fast doing this.'

'I mean, obviously he's had more training than me, so who knows what would happen if I actually had the time to commit to improving my strength?' Uncle Harry stretched out his arms, staring at his fingertips.

'I'm surprised he asked us if we work out,' Daddy said, visibly tensing his stomach, then slapping it with his hand. 'That's really quite solid, you know.'

'Pipe down, ladies,' Mummy said. 'Some of us are trying to work.'

I ran around a bit to join in. I don't know this Usain

Bolt character, but I could probably take him. I am pretty fast, you know. For someone who has only been walking for about two months.

'We ought to consider,' Mummy was saying to the Shine Supervisor from her Hair Team, 'that if we increase the level, it may actually blind people.'

'Mm, mm,' the Shine Supervisor nodded. 'We don't want to intimidate.'

'Well . . .' Mummy said, raising her eyebrows.

'Ah. I see what you mean, Ma'am,' the Shine Supervisor said, nodding knowingly. 'Why fight what is inevitable?'

'Quite,' Mummy said.

Uncle Harry then said he'd like to practise his speech on us, so while I was chasing Lupo, he started to read. 'I am honoured to be here today to support the work done on behalf of the wild flora and fauna of sub-Saharan Africa,' he started.

'Really good. Strong opening,' Daddy said supportively. He gets tremendously serious about speeches.

'I am in awe of the commitment this group of incredible guys have shown to these endangered plants.'

'Rhinos,' Mummy said.

'What?'

'Endangered rhinos. Plants is next week.'

Uncle Harry took out his pen. 'Rhinos,' he muttered, writing something on his piece of paper and putting a line through something else.

'Wait – I thought I was doing rhinos?' Daddy said.

'Spike's doing rhinos, you're doing elephants,' Mummy said.

'What are you doing?' Uncle Harry asked.

Mummy sighed. 'This does all the talking,' she said, and shook out her hair.

Everyone stopped what they were doing and went quiet. I saw my Latin teacher start to reach his hand towards Mummy's hair, but my Diary Secretary slapped it down. 'Don't be a fool, John,' he whispered sharply.

'I just worry I'm not doing enough for these animals,' Daddy said anxiously. 'It's a shame I can't . . . grow my own tusks to show my support.'

'Can someone look into that, please?' Mummy said.

There was a scurry of notes made.

Daddy really loves animals, which is why he doesn't mind his nickname being Wombat. He thinks wombats are marvellous. He gets terribly upset if people are mean to any animal and tries to help them whenever he can.

'Knowing what it was like to have tusks would make me feel even closer to the elephants,' Daddy said. 'Remember when you had that beard, Spike?'

'Yeah,' Uncle Harry said. 'It really made me feel a lot closer to people who have beards.'

'Well, there you go,' Daddy said.

'Sir,' said Daddy's Private Secretary, 'in the absence of finding anything that can actually give you your – ahem – *own* tusks, perhaps we can look into prosthetics?'

'That's a good idea,' Daddy said. 'Maybe we could turn it into an annual thing, like when people grow moustaches in November, except we could get everyone to wear tusks. We could call it *Tuskcember*.'

'I would totally do that,' Uncle Harry said.

'Babykins? If you wore tusks, this thing would really catch fire and become an actual *thing*.'

'You know who would send this through the roof, though?' Uncle Harry said.

They all looked at me.

'Small G in a set of small tusks. Imagine the impact.'

'It would go global,' Daddy whispered.

'Headline news,' Mummy agreed. 'Even in the countries where they don't have news.'

My team started to wildly discuss the idea.

'If we have a prototype made, we can start testing it,' my head of Global Strategy said.

'We'd have to notify all the wildlife charities. The likelihood is, elephants and rhinos will become so popular that we're at risk of overrunning Africa and parts of Asia with them,' said my Zoologist.

'We'll need to alert Downing Street – the Prime Minister may want to give the UN a heads-up,' said my director of Political Communications.

'We could do a soft launch with some elephant-logo knitwear,' my stylist said. 'I don't even dare mention rhino fancy dress because I don't think the internet could cope with it.'

'Yes, yes, let's not lose our heads,' my Press Secretary said. 'This is about supporting wildlife, not bringing down the world's global communication network. Prince George in rhino fancy dress would literally blow up people's computers.'

The thing is, these people are right. Even I know that me dressed as a rhino would be too much. It's far better to drip-feed these things. I remember those Early Day pre-walker shoes I wore crashing websites and they weren't even the main feature of my outfit that time.

'This is great, everyone,' Daddy said, looking pleased. 'Let's hope that by Christmas we're all sitting in this exact same room, in these exact same clothes –'

'Er, I don't think so,' Mummy said. 'I've already re-cycled this dress twice.'

'Not in these exact same clothes, but at this exact same time, all wearing prosthetic tusks to support the endangered elephants, rhinos and horned creatures of this world.'

'Cool idea,' Uncle Harry said. 'Very cool. Pa might do it, you know.'

'Mills *definitely* would,' Daddy said.

'Someone should ask G-Pop,' Mummy said wryly.

'Christ!' Uncle Harry said. 'Nothing on this earth would induce me to do that.'

Mummy turned to him and started to smile.

'Oh no, no, no – no, you don't,' Uncle Harry said, waving his finger at Mummy. 'Do not say those words.'

'I dare you,' Mummy said gleefully.

'Arrrgh!' Uncle Harry said, smacking his hand across his forehead. 'He'll make a coat-stand out of me, mate.'

'I *double* dare you,' Mummy said, cackling.

'Damn you, Middleton.' Uncle Harry put his head in his hands.

Mummy and Uncle Harry have a strange rule about dares. They dare each other to do outrageous things and whoever loses has to sit next to Great Aunt Annie at the next family dinner and incorporate a horse-related word or phrase into everything they say to her. In fact, they enjoy this challenge so much, they sometimes just do it anyway. Uncle Harry always opens with 'Hay, Aunt A!' when it's his turn because that's an immediate point.

They've done a lot of different dares. One time, Mummy says she dared Uncle Harry to run through the Picture Gallery at HQ with no clothes on just as the public were queuing up to come in for the Leonardo da Vinci: Anatomist exhibition. Daddy was so worried and kept saying, 'This is a terrible, terrible idea,' but Uncle Harry didn't seem that fazed.

'This isn't a dare. It's a recreational pleasure,' he said, ripping off his clothes and streaking past da Vinci's studies of the human body with a great cry of 'Get a load of that, Leo!'

Anyway, Uncle Harry is panicking about how he is going to get G-Pop to agree to wearing the tusks. He says he may have to attach a note to me and send me in to see G-Pop like a carrier pigeon so that he doesn't have to be in the building when G-Pop reads the request.

August 2014

3rd August

Today I had one of my ancestry classes and it was about a very distant relative called Richard III.

This is what I learnt. Richard III had black hair and was generally quite cross a lot of the time. Apparently he might or might not have had a hump, and might or might not have been quite unkind to his two nephews – and by unkind, I mean he might have had them killed and buried at the bottom of the stairs at the Tower of London. I suppose he never played football with them, like Uncle Harry does with me. Or baked them a cake for no reason like Uncle J sometimes does.

My Ancestral History teacher says Richard III died in battle when someone bashed him on the head, took all his clothes away and eventually buried him under a car park in Leicester. Somebody found his bones last year and now they've moved him to the cathedral. Must have been embarrassing for him if he wasn't wearing anything.

Worst of all, he may or may not have ganged up with his brother Edward and had their other brother drowned in a vat of wine. That brother's name was *George*! Arrrrgh! So relieved I don't have a brother – yikes!

Mummy is being a bit funny today. She didn't want to eat any lunch and she had to go to sleep this afternoon, which was odd because we usually do art class together and she never misses that.

4th August

Mummy and Daddy are in Belgium today because of the First World War. My stylist dressed me in the traditional Belgian costume of a beret and smock for my Skype call with them before supper. I like to show an interest in their trips, even when my schedule doesn't allow me to join them, because it's important to be supportive. Not my favourite costume, but my stylist said it was either that or they'd have to dress me as a waffle.

Daddy was normal, chatting away, but at one point Mummy suddenly got up, covering her mouth with her hand, and ran off somewhere and it made Daddy look worried, but he didn't say anything.

Perhaps she realized she wanted some waffles.

8th August

This weekend we are staying with Goonie and GaGa at Highgrove. Mummy was lying down again this morning, so Daddy and I went to see Goonie in the Kitchen Garden and we found him among the runner beans. Talking to them as usual.

'You are looking tremendously strong and lean, if I might say so,' he was saying cheerfully. 'Isn't the weather glorious? Got any plans for the bank holiday?'

It is important to have good manners at all times, no matter whom you are talking to. When GG tries to tell Goonie that this doesn't include plants, he gets very agitated. He loves his garden so much that in good weather he sleeps in a large tent by the Thyme Walk. That way, he can just step out into nature every morning and watch the butterflies as he has breakfast on the lawn. As well as talking to the herbs about his dreams and asking how they slept, etc.

'Ah, Georgie!' he said, when he saw me. 'Come and meet these lettuces. I've been telling them all about you.'

The lettuces didn't say much – they didn't say anything, actually – but Goonie didn't seem to mind.

'This is my grandson, Prince George of Cambridge,' he said to them. 'But I just call him Georgie – right, old thing?' he said, beaming at me. 'I wanted him to call me Grandpa, but it's ended up as Goonie. One can never control these things as one should like to.'

'You know why, Pa,' Daddy said.

'Enter Bluebottle. Waits for audience applause. Not a sausage,' Goonie said, in a funny squeaky voice, then roared with laughter. 'The Goons just are so wonderfully funny . . .' He pulled up a couple of carrots from the soil by their green tops. 'These carrots have been so excited all week about you coming to stay,' he told me, 'haven't you, Carrots? "Yes, we have!"' he said, in another squeaky voice, waggling them in my face. ' "Hello, Georgie! We like your sun-hat!" '

Then we talked to the onions and Goonie sang the aubergines a song by his favourite singer, Leonard Cohen, swaying a bit and tapping his hand against his leg.

'OK, thanks, Pa,' Daddy said, going a bit pink.

'Don't be shy, join in!' Goonie said.

'I'm more of a Linkin Park man myself,' Daddy said.

'Having a little singalong behind my back, you devils!' a loud gravelly voice suddenly piped up behind us. 'You know how I adore a singalong.'

It was GaGa, who was wearing a full beekeeping suit.

'Just popping down to the hives to get some bee venom – thought Kate and I could do a face mask later,' she said cheerfully. 'Then I was lured off my path by a Siren Song.'

'Did you look in on her?' Daddy asked anxiously.

'Yes – poor darling was worshipping the porcelain goddess,' GaGa said.

Daddy and Goonie looked confused.

'You know – talking to God on the big white telephone.'

They still looked totally blank.

'She was being sick,' GaGa said, shaking her head. 'Honestly, you people need to get out more.'

GaGa is a highly knowledgeable person. She's always saying things that other members of the family don't understand and that's because she used to live what Goonie refers to as 'over the wall'. That's where Mummy comes from, too, and it's one of the reasons they're such firm friends. Along with the fact that GaGa is what Uncle Harry calls 'the original ghetto superstar'.

'Poor girl – bug, is it?' Goonie asked. 'How's your health these days?' he said to a turnip.

'Yes, I think so,' Daddy said, sounding funny and his cheeks went pink again.

GaGa raised her eyebrows, like she'd suddenly understood something, but she didn't say anything. At least, I think she did – it was quite hard to tell with the beekeeping veil.

'Get someone to take up a cushion if she has to keep kneeling on the bathroom floor like that,' Goonie said.

'Yes, Sir,' the Cushion Carrier said.

Goonie has a cushion carrier. He makes sure

Goonie's favourite cushion is always near, in case he wants to sit down.

'Oh, there you are,' Goonie said, pretending to clutch his heart in surprise. The Cushion Carrier is so quiet, you sometimes forget he's there. He stood holding the cushion on another cushion.

Anyway, GaGa went off to see her bees and Daddy and I built a house made of twigs for me to play with. Goonie was very impressed with it. 'It's innately beautiful,' he said, as Daddy added some grass to the roof. 'It's a physical manifestation of the Divine Order of the Universe.'

In fact, he then sat down on his cushion and painted a watercolour of it. His Watercolour Carrier is always on hand, too, in case inspiration strikes and he wants to paint.

When GaGa came back, we picked some peas and ate them straight from the pod, which I always like doing with her, even though I find most green food pretty disgusting. She fed them to me and we sang songs and had such a nice time that we didn't realize how many peas we'd eaten until I was sick absolutely everywhere.

'I hate to say it,' GaGa said, 'but I think Georgie might need a . . .'

There was silence.

'No,' Daddy whispered.

'Surely not,' Goonie gasped.

'Yes,' GaGa said. 'A bath.'

Daddy put his head into his hands.

I don't know what all the fuss was about. I love baths!

In fact, I love baths so much that I try to make them as fun for everyone else as they are for me. What could be more brilliant than splashing in water, smacking your hands through the bubbles, throwing your ducks, constantly attempting to get up and slipping so much that it makes everyone shriek with anxiety, refusing to let anyone wash your hair, trying to eat the sponge, pushing your fingers up the taps, pulling the plug and screaming when they try to get you out.

Bathtime is my favourite time of day. I was very excited that this might be happening early, so I shouted and ran around and all the dogs started barking.

'Maybe I can just wipe him down,' Daddy said desperately.

'I don't know about these things, of course,' Goonie said, 'but if Mills says he needs a bath, then . . .'

'Come on,' GaGa said, picking me up. 'It's nothing I haven't done a hundred times.'

'But the Bath Team have got the weekend off,' Daddy said. 'And Kate isn't well. It's a minimum two-man job.'

'Use my Bath Team?' Goonie offered.

'I'll help you,' GaGa said. 'He's in the zone with his vegetables,' she added, nodding to Goonie. 'We won't get a sensible word out of him again until teatime.'

Goonie looked at her in the way that Daddy looks at

Mummy, which is how Lupo looks when he knows he will get a treat for not barking at GG's security detail, and then he sang a drippy Leonard song about dancing until the end of love or something.

'Get back to your beans, Fred,' GaGa laughed. 'You're exhausting.'

GaGa is definitely Goonie's best friend. Along with his delphiniums.

About half an hour later, when GaGa and Daddy were kneeling in front of me in a large lake of water, both completely drenched, and I was sliding around on the soap, GaGa turned to Daddy, who was wringing out his shirt, and said, 'It's at times like this that I wish I hadn't given up fags.'

I only saw Mummy for a bit today because she said she was still feeling odd. Even then she kept running out of the room and making funny noises in the bathroom, growling, 'Holy Jesus Christ,' over and over.

Maybe she ate too many peas as well. Even though she hasn't come out of her room today. So that doesn't make sense . . .

9th August

'I know it's silly,' Goonie said today at breakfast, 'but it still baffles me that people think I have seven eggs prepared for breakfast,' as the footmen brought in two trays of Duchy Originals organic free-range eggs and laid all eighteen of them in front of him.

'Who could possibly choose the right one from only seven?' He shook his head.

Mummy silently nibbled on some dry Duchy Originals rye and sunflower toast.

'Eeny, meeny, miny, mo . . .' Goonie muttered, going along the row, tapping each one gently on the top.

'You know what the press are like,' GaGa said, tucking into her Duchy Originals bacon. 'They probably think the footmen clean your teeth for you.'

That's so silly because they only squeeze out the toothpaste onto his toothbrush.

Mummy gave me a Duchy Originals muffin. She looked a bit sort of grey.

'Are you OK?' Daddy asked.

'Do not speak to me,' Mummy said queasily. 'Never speak to me again.'

'I know what you need, Kate, darling,' Goonie said. 'You need to spend some time with my buddies the buddleias. August is their month. The butterflies have gone quite wild for them – that's my kind of bedlam. Tell them how you're feeling – they're tremendously good listeners.'

'Fred?' GaGa piped up.

'Yes, Gladys?' Goonie replied.

'Do be quiet.'

Goonie laughed. 'Isn't she marvellous?' he said to

me. 'Always putting me in my place. Never happened to me until I met her. I adore it.'

We had to go after breakfast because Daddy had a lot of work to do. Mummy seemed to be in quite a cross mood on the way home, which is not like her at all. A couple of times, she shouted, 'Stop the car!' and Daddy had to pull over so she could rush out, get on her knees and look very closely at the grass. It caused total chaos with our security team, who kept having to section off parts of the motorway and form human shields so Mummy couldn't be seen. I just fed Lupo my rice cakes and let him play with my fire engine. The one that someone called Winston Churchill gave to Goonie when he was born.

14th August

Today I had polo class. Daddy, Uncle Harry and Goonie are all mega polo fans, so I'm learning the ropes to carry on the tradition. At the moment, I'm practising with my rocking horse using a plastic mallet, but I'm excited to play with the real mallet my friend President Obama gave me when I was born. The one that was made from a tree on the south lawn of the White House – and if my lapis-lazuli orb from the Pope didn't have that big old Edward the Confessor silver cross on it, I could use it as a ball.

I haven't met the Pope yet, but I think we would get along very well. I had to wear a long whitish dress when I was christened (arrrgh, do *not* remind me) and that was for just a few hours. He has to wear a long white dress every day. TRAUMA. What happens if he spills apple juice down it, like I did down mine? Like THAT was an accident #thatwasnoaccident.

Daddy is busy with his air-ambulance pilot training. He spends a lot of time with his air-ambulance books and he will have to do fourteen exams and a lot of other tests.

Mummy also did a test today. I'm not sure what it was for, but I heard them talking about it. She definitely passed because she looked really happy. Daddy must have helped her with it because he said, 'We hit the bullseye, Babykins!' Then Mummy had to go and lie down. I suppose doing tests can make you feel quite tired.

16th August

Uncle Harry has a new name for Mummy.

'Where's Barfing Betty?' he asked Daddy, when he came to see us today.

As it turned out Mummy was lying on the floor in the middle of the room. We keep finding her like that all over the house, and if someone tries to help her get up, she refuses. A memo has gone round asking people not to comment, that it's better to say nothing and just to step over her until further notice.

Uncle Harry started making 'bleeeuuuuurgh' noises and heaving over the back of the sofa and Mummy sat up briefly to throw a cushion at him and tell him to shut up and then she lay down again. I think she is still feeling sick from those peas we ate at Highgrove – although it's odd because I don't actually remember even seeing her in the garden once during the entire weekend . . . Anyway, I was playing with my orb from the Pope when Uncle Harry said he'd had an idea.

'Let's create a mock scenario where a person might require an air ambulance,' he said cheerfully. 'Puking Pamela can be the patient.'

'Don't make me have to kill you,' Mummy said, without opening her eyes.

'Listen to her,' Uncle Harry laughed. 'She's like an evil rug.'

'What should I do?' Daddy asked seriously.

'You go and wait in your air-ambulance corner over there,' Uncle Harry said, pointing to the doorway. 'I'll set the scene. It's late at night.' He closed the curtains. 'Small G and I have spent the evening embedded in the pub playing darts over a few pints and we've decided to take a walk together on a nearby mountain to sober up. But, hang on, the weather's atrocious and we're now lost.' He picked me up and we lurched round the room a bit together.

'Careful of that Queen Anne chest,' Mummy said, with her eyes closed.

'That's not a Queen Anne chest – it's a roadblock, which means no vehicles can get up to this rocky place we now find ourselves in,' Uncle Harry said dramatically.

'I'd prefer it if you didn't take George to the pub, just while we're talking about this,' Daddy said. 'He's far too young to be drinking.'

'I'm not going to,' Uncle Harry said, sounding exasperated. 'And he hasn't *really* been drinking. I know he walks like a drunk but don't hold that against him.'

Mummy propped herself up on one elbow. 'Don't worry about me, I'm fine,' she said, sounding like she wasn't fine.

'No, you're not, you're lying on the ground in the middle of a forest and in need of medical attention,' Uncle Harry said. 'Why is no one listening to me?'

'You said it was rocks and a mountain,' Daddy said, rushing over to Mummy. 'Are you all right, Babykins?'

'Excuse me, we haven't called the air ambulance yet – get back to your corner immediately,' Uncle Harry said.

'Sorry, sorry.' Daddy went and stood in his corner again.

'As I was saying, it's a very rocky forest,' Uncle Harry

41

said. 'On a mountain. Small G and I are trying to navigate our way through this terrible thunderstorm and, oh look, we appear to have come across the body of a vomiting woman.'

Uncle Harry put me down and I ran over to Mummy. I prodded her face, stuck my fingers in her mouth and rolled my orb around her a bit in case that cheered her up, but all she did was take a lot of deep breaths and rub her stomach.

'That's right, Small G, check her airways,' Uncle Harry said. 'Although if she spews, she's on her own. I can't be doing with any of that.'

'You have no idea,' Mummy said, with her eyes still shut.

'This woman needs an ambulance!' Uncle Harry shouted. 'But no ambulances will ever make it past that Queen Anne roadblock. We're in the middle of nowhere. What are we going to do? We need an AIR ambulance – *only one man can save us.*' He looked at Daddy. 'Well, come on then – that's your cue.'

Daddy stood where he was. 'What is?'

'Hurling Helen needs your help. You have to come and rescue us.'

'You haven't rung to report it yet,' Daddy said.

Mummy opened one of her eyes with a big sigh. 'I'll ring.'

'You can't ring, you're unconscious,' Uncle Harry said. 'Small G can do it.'

Uncle Harry gave me his phone. I sucked it a bit and waved it around.

'Make sure you ask for Willy the Flying Wombat. Then maybe we'll make it out of this rocky, foresty mountain-hell-hole.'

I gabbled into the phone, like I see them doing all the time.

Uncle Harry turned to Daddy. 'You have to pretend to answer,' he said, in a loud whisper.

'Right!' Daddy said. He took his phone out of his pocket. 'Hello? This is the Air Ambulance Service. How may I help you?'

'Tell him we have discovered a human vomit-volcano, and if he doesn't come this instant, she's going to start an avalanche,' Uncle Harry said to me.

I chattered into the phone and pressed a few things on it.

'Have you checked her airways?' Daddy asked.

'Yes, yes, yes, we did that ages ago,' Uncle Harry said, frustrated.

'OK, is she conscious?'

'Someone get me a bucket and I mean NOW,' Mummy said, in a scary voice.

Uncle Harry took the phone from me.

'Now listen here,' he said into it. 'This is an emergency. We need immediate assistance. We are seconds away from an eruption.'

'Please stay calm, Sir,' Daddy said, into his phone,

from the corner of the room. 'I'm just trying to see if anyone's free to come and rescue you.'

'We don't want anyone, we want you,' Uncle Harry said to Daddy. 'That's the point.'

'I realize you're feeling anxious, but I can assure you help will be on its way as soon as possible. I can keep you company in the mean time.'

'Wait – what? I don't want a friendly chat – I want you to get in the flipping helicopter and fly over here to rescue us.'

'I can't do that, Sir – I'm not qualified,' Daddy tried to explain.

'Yes, you are,' Uncle Harry shouted. 'Chop, chop!'

'I can't fly unsupervised,' Daddy explained.

'So ask your imaginary pilot friend to come with you,' Uncle Harry said, throwing his hands up in the air. 'Do I have to think of everything?'

'OK – I'll see if he's on duty. Please hold the line, Sir, while I contact my colleague, Captain . . . um . . . Kirk?'

'You can't ask Captain Kirk – he flies a spaceship, not a helicopter,' Uncle Harry said. 'In fact, he doesn't even fly that spaceship, someone else does.'

'It's a . . . different Captain Kirk.'

I noticed that Mummy had quietly started crawling quickly out of the room.

'Where do you think you're going?' Uncle Harry shouted after her. 'I just called you an air ambulance.'

She didn't stop to say anything but flashed what

looked like her middle finger as she disappeared on all fours round the corner.

'That's a relief,' Daddy said.

'What?'

'I've just realized I don't have Captain Kirk's number.'

Uncle Harry just pushed him over when he said that.

19th August

So, listen to this – I've found out that one day I will be Commander-in-Chief of all the British Armed Forces! They told me in Military Study. At the moment, it's GG's job. Then it will be Goonie's. Then it will be Daddy's. Then it will be mine. ALL MINE. Mwaaaah haaa haaa haaa haaaaaaa!

I'm working on several plans for how I'll use them when they're not serving the nation. For example, I'll ask the navy to help me find buried treasure and dinosaurs. The army will be good for building fortresses, like the one Uncle Harry built for me out of pillows – and I think I'll ask the air force to take me to visit my crocodile in Darwin.

GG loves being head of the Armed Forces and they always put on a show for her. She even had to inspect Daddy and Uncle Harry for their passing-out parades. They both said it was a disaster, because GG knew it would make them hysterical so on both occasions she deliberately made a beeline for them, flashing them with big saucer eyes. Uncle Harry said he was trying so hard not to laugh that he actually pulled a muscle in his own mouth. Daddy was just relieved she didn't do any of her impressions – if GG had broken into her legendary Scouse accent, Daddy might *actually* have passed out, which is not what's supposed to happen at all.

It's typical of GG – she's always looking for LOLZ. When everything is always arranged perfectly for you, it can be fun when things go wrong. She and G-Pop love practical jokes – they used to constantly try to trip each other up in front of important presidents in the early days, and now they like to hide each other's glasses, usually before one of them has to give a speech – the State Opening of Parliament is a particular tradition. This is the kind of thing that great-grandparents enjoy in life, I suppose, even when they're five hundred million years old like G-Pop is.

22nd August

Mummy came and played with me this afternoon. She looked sort of greyish-yellow and kept having to stop for rests, taking deep breaths and sipping iced water. She also has five new members of staff – they are her Personal Bowl Carriers. They are around her at all times, so that when she feels the need, she can stick her head in one of these silver bowls and make that odd roaring sound she's now so fond of.

Maybe she has teeth coming through, like I do. They are pretty sore and they can make me feel a bit moody, so I'm sympathetic.

26th August

Mummy is now almost bright green and she has been wearing the same onesie for three days. Aunt P and Uncle J came and visited her today. She was sprawled in the middle of the corridor refusing to move, as usual, so Aunt P and Uncle J had to just sit on the floor next to her.

'Look, I made you some marshmallows with your face on them!' Uncle J said, opening a box.

'For the love of God,' was all Mummy could croak.

They didn't stay long, actually.

29th August

There was an actual fight in Mummy's bathroom today! Daddy once said that Mummy's hair could end wars but now it has actually started one! So exciting!!!

Mummy, it turns out, has not been shouting all this time. She just keeps being sick. So it MUST be those peas. She was in the middle of a big wave of sickness in her bathroom today, but managed to find a moment to say, 'I might need someone to hold my hair back if that's OK.'

You should have seen the reaction. It was a full stampede. All five of the Personal Bowl Carriers immediately dropped their bowls, rushing towards her, but, like lightning, her stylist stuck her leg out and tripped one of them up, causing a pile-up, before trampling over them to get to Mummy first. The Diary Secretary pushed over the Media Manager, as the Make-up Artist physically wrestled the Speechwriter to the floor, slapping him so hard he became totally disoriented and walked straight into the shower door, knocking himself out. The whole of the Hair Team were pulling each other's hair and fighting and everyone was shouting, 'ME! LET ME HOLD IT BACK!!' It was chaos. Mummy had to push her panic button, and in a matter of seconds, the police had arrived with her security detail and everyone was detained and given a caution. Maria Teresa and I had only dropped in to give Mummy a kiss, so we saw the whole thing – it was amazing!

After that there had to be an emergency meeting. I heard one of Mummy's security detail telling one of my security detail that the Hair Team had shouted all the way through, saying Mummy's hair was their jurisdiction and no one else had any right to touch it. Then the Hair Therapist said, well, actually, it should really just be her responsibility because she'd built up a special level of trust with the hair that no one else understood – and the Shine Supervisor got cross and said that that relationship was in no way physical like hers was and therefore she should be the one designated to take care of the hair's needs because it was used to her hands.

The Washing Division then went wild, saying *they* were the ones who handled Mummy's hair the most and who did these other people think they were – but then one of the Personal Bowl Carriers pointed out that it had been an open question, 'I might need *someone* to hold my hair back', which suggested a major lack of professionalism on behalf of the Hair Team, because why would Mummy not just ask one of them outright and why weren't they all carrying hairbands anyway? This made the Hair Team pretty furious and another scuffle broke out, with one of them shouting, 'Do not tell me how to do my job!' They had to be separated by the security detail again and restrained by the police. People are actually talking about pressing charges!

It's all tremendously thrilling, but Mummy has decided that she's going to have to work on a rotation cycle, letting everyone have the opportunity to hold her hair back at some point. Any other decision would cause endless problems and in-fighting because jealousy would run riot.

A rota has been drawn up and, as a result, three people must be with Mummy on hair duty, in addition to their normal jobs, at any one time in case she needs them to hold her hair at a moment's notice. The first time a volunteer's help was called for was after suppertime today. I was playing in Mummy and Daddy's room, trying to brush Lupo with Mummy's silver engraved hairbrush (the one made with hair from Desert Orchid's tail), when she started feeling funny and had to run to the bathroom. It was her Media Manager's turn to hold her hair, but when they came out of the bathroom, he still had it firmly in his hands – a strange, bewitched look in his eye.

Mummy seemed sort of tense and said, 'Thank you so much, you can let go now,' but he just tightened his grip. Mummy tugged a bit, trying to loosen his hold, but it made no difference. She finally had to prise his fingers open one by one, while her Hair Supervisor said to him, 'I know it's a lot to take in, but try to stay calm.'

'So soft . . . so shiny . . .' was all he could mutter, as he was bundled out of the room by two security guards.

Daddy has said they might have to have some kind of brief course to know what to expect and how to manage their feelings about Mummy's hair because this total lack of control isn't working and people are becoming undignified in their hysteria. 'It's not that I don't understand,' Daddy said to Mummy. 'I do – it's just I think we need to provide support for them. They're all obviously so overwhelmed.'

Mummy just sighed and said, 'Like *that*'s news.'

September 2014

1st September

A lot of peculiar things are happening around here. I'm now starting to wonder if those peas at Highgrove were poisonous, although I'm fine and so is GaGa. I know this because she sent Mummy a card that arrived today. Daddy read it out to her at breakfast. It said,

Darling K

I knew it!!!!!
    Such wonderful news!!!
    Make sure those lazy boys are looking after you – so sorry you're feeling like hell on a stick.
    Keep your pecker up!
    Laters.

Love Mills xxx

PS Try eating strawberry ice cream – always worked for me. I'll have some Duchy Originals sent over.

It came with an enormous bunch of flowers and a note saying, 'It is impossible to feel sick when in the presence of dahlias. Fact! Love Charles'.

I'm not sure that's true, though, because Mummy was sick into the milk jug shortly afterwards.

She is constantly on the phone to Granny C too – she keeps saying things like, 'I can't keep anything down, not even air. Even the thought of breathing makes me want to hurl,' and 'My hormones are out of control. I feel unhinged – like Bertha Mason at full moon,' and 'It's a bit early to talk about names.'

Why would Granny C want to talk about names? She already has one . . .

2nd September

Daddy says Mummy has gone for a playdate at the hospital. Daddy sometimes looks worried and sometimes excited. Uncle Harry keeps hitting him on the back saying, 'Who's the Daddy?' Why would he say that? We know Daddy is the Daddy.

4th September

I was at HQ today. David is back. He told GG he has been on holiday and came to see us sporting a healthy tan.

'I've missed you!' he said gleefully when the tea tray was brought in.

'I've missed you too,' GG said, smirking.

David went terribly red.

'I do apologise, Ma'am,' he said, shifting self-consciously in his chair. 'It goes without saying, I greatly missed our weekly meetings, which I always look forward to and thoroughly enjoy. Your advice and wisdom are invaluable and to have this time together is a privilege.'

GG nodded.

'And of course, the sandwiches are a great treat.'

'I'm glad to hear it,' GG said. 'I do hope you enjoyed your holiday.'

'Yes, we did, thank you,' David said. 'Probably too many Cornish pasties, though.' He patted his stomach. 'Might have to do something about that at some point. George Osborne says he might go on a diet and some people think he's already thinner than me . . .'

He paused, waiting for GG to say something.

'I've always thought we were sort of the same weight, but . . . ?'

'I haven't seen the Chancellor in a while,' GG said, 'but I'm sure you're right.'

'I could Google a picture of him, if you like? Then you can compare us,' David said, getting his iPhone out. 'Those number-crunchers have big appetites!' He laughed incredibly loudly.

'Maybe later,' GG said. 'And now, Prime Minister, perhaps we ought to turn our attention to other things.'

'Ah – yes – the scones!' David said. 'I haven't had one of those for ages.'

'I was actually referring to the Referendum.'

'Of course,' said David, blushing and helping himself to three scones.

Then they talked about Scotland: will they, won't they, blah blah – I don't really know what it's all about. And then some kind of 'timely news'. David said to GG that it could 'literally save the union' and GG said, 'Well, we could probably do that by photographing George in a kilt. Let's bear it in mind.'

A kilt is a kind of skirt, I've just learnt. Goonie and G-Pop are fond of them, and obviously I don't want to wear one, but I'll do it if I have to because that's what it means to be Royal. You put your personal feelings aside for the sake of your country, and that includes Scotland because that's the bit at the top that GG loves.

Anyway, Goonie spent the day with my pal President Obama at the 'Welcome the World to Wales' reception in Newport as part of the NATO summit and Goonie rang Daddy this evening and then he handed the phone over to President Obama. Daddy kept saying, 'Thank you, thank you,' and 'Yes, we're very excited,' and 'Kate's feeling a lot better.'

'NO, I'M NOT,' Mummy shouted, from where she was lying in the doorway.

Daddy laughed awkwardly. 'She says thanks so much for asking after her – we're so excited about our visit to the States in December.'

'I'M NOT,' Mummy shouted again. 'I'M NEVER LEAVING THIS DOORWAY.'

'That was Kate saying how excited she is too,' Daddy said. 'Love to Michelle and the girls from all of us. Lupo says hi to Bo and Sunny.'

After that Mummy crawled off, and Daddy just looked at me and said, 'It's all my fault,' but I didn't know what that meant.

5th September

Granny C and Grandpa M visited us today. Grandpa M disappeared behind the curtains at one point, emerging in his inflatable sumo costume, which he made Daddy blow up. He suggested we do a conga to help cheer Mummy up, putting on a song called 'Feelin' Hot, Hot, Hot' but no one except me wanted to join in. Lupo ran around barking and Daddy tapped his foot a bit because he didn't want to be impolite, but Mummy didn't move from the floor. She just lay completely still and said, 'Shoot me now.'

At that point Granny C sent Grandpa M out of the room and told him to wait in the car, but he got completely stuck in the doorframe because his costume was so big, and Daddy had to ring down to the kitchen for someone to come up with a skewer so he could be punctured and deflated. It was the first time I have seen Mummy really laugh for ages.

6th September

Happy birthday, Aunt P!!! She is THIRTY-ONE years old!!! She'll need to take rests when she climbs the stairs!!!

She came round to see us today so we could give her our presents. Her cake had just been brought in and we were singing happy birthday to her when Uncle Harry arrived. 'What's happening here then?' he asked.

'It's P's birthday,' Daddy said.

'What? No one told me.'

'Actually I texted you about it yesterday,' Mummy said.

'Ah,' Uncle Harry said. 'I won't have seen that. You're gagging me out so much with your vomit stories at the moment that I'm not really reading your texts.'

'Don't worry,' Aunt P said cheerfully. 'I barely remembered myself.'

'Well, it's not right that I shouldn't give you a birthday present,' Uncle Harry said, 'and seeing as I've turned up empty handed, I'll have to improvise.' He looked around the room. 'Take that off, please,' he said, pointing at Daddy's jumper.

Daddy took it off.

'What about this?' Uncle Harry said, offering it to Aunt P. 'This is a nice jumper. It would look much better on you than it does on Wombat.'

'It's not actually mine,' Daddy said. 'I borrowed it from Pa.'

Uncle Harry put it down and continued to scour the room. He found a copy of *Tatler* magazine lying on the table. 'OK, then, what about this? Some interesting articles here – "How posh is your body?" and "Help! I inherited a castle!"'

'That would have made an excellent present,' Aunt P said. 'Were it not for the fact I already have a subscription to *Tatler*.'

'Girls are so hard to shop for . . .' Uncle Harry muttered as he stepped over me to where Mummy was sitting on the sofa. He picked up a very expensive-looking handbag that was on the floor by her feet. 'Well, this looks perfect to me. You people love this sort of thing, don't you? Nice leather, shiny insides – it's got gold bits that I don't really understand hanging off the side,' he said. 'This has to be a winner.'

'It is,' Mummy said, 'and it's also the handbag P gave me for my birthday.'

Uncle Harry came and picked me up and held me

out to Aunt P. 'This baby?' he said. 'He's an all right bloke.'

'He is,' Mummy said. 'And I'd quite like to keep him, actually.'

Uncle Harry stood with his hands on his hips and thought. 'Well,' he said. 'There's clearly only one option left.' He got down on one knee.

'Oh my God, what's happening?' Daddy gasped.

'Pippa Adorable Middleton,' Uncle Harry said, taking Aunt P's hand. 'You're the cutest girl I ever met. Much nicer than your sister and I'm not just saying that because of your arse. Will you make me the happiest man on the planet and accept my hand in marriage as your birthday present? And then we can upstage these jokers and become the world's most beloved couple, like Burton and Taylor, but without the drunk fighting.'

Aunt P frowned thoughtfully.

'Interesting that you're having to consider this,' Uncle Harry said. 'Let me help with that. OK, so where to begin with our many similarities? I'm extremely sporty, like you. I like parties, like you – and we both look good in red. Although to be honest, I'm probably slightly ahead of you in that. I'm also very good with children and babies. Just ask Small G, he'll tell you.'

'What should I do, George?' Aunt P asked me. 'Say yes or no?'

I personally think it would be an excellent idea if

Uncle Harry and Aunt P got married – so I handed Aunt P my tractor to show that she had my blessing.

'That is a clear sign that G approves,' Uncle Harry said. 'He usually hits the roof if anyone goes near that thing. Come on, P. It's what the nation wants.'

'Just a couple of queries,' Aunt P said. 'First – there's no ring.'

'I was hoping that the profoundly romantic nature and spontaneity of the moment might help you overlook that,' Uncle Harry said.

'The ignorance is astounding . . .' Mummy said, shaking her head.

'Second,' Aunt P said. 'I might have to run your suggestion past my boyfriend.'

'All right, all right,' Uncle Harry said, getting up, 'and a lovely chap he is too. But let's just make sure we find out what his intentions are because you've now got options. Very clever, handsome and excellent at dancing options, I think we'd all agree.'

'I definitely will,' Aunt P said, patting Uncle Harry on the shoulder. 'And thanks for telling me I don't look as good in red as you do.'

'Honesty is the foundation of every successful marriage,' Uncle Harry said.

Mummy looked at Daddy. 'Are you crying?' she said.

'No,' Daddy squeaked, wiping his eyes. 'No, I'm not. It's just good to know romance isn't dead.'

'Which is more than can be said for how your arm is

going to feel in about three seconds,' Uncle Harry said, taking a running jump at him and knocking him over behind the sofa.

In other news, Mummy and Daddy's teams have literally gone berserk. They worked all through the night and are rushing around having emergency meetings. They keep talking about 'the announcement' and 'the global repercussions' – I think they're planning something very big wardrobe-wise for me. We can all guess what that means. I'm going to have to save Scotland by wearing a kilt. Oh well.

7th September

They don't want me to wear a kilt.

They want me TO BE A BROTHER.

Mummy is having a baby.

Arrrgh!

How did I get this so wrong????????

My mind is all over the shop.

OK, George – settle down. Breathe. Focus.

I'll go back to the beginning.

I had just finished my fencing class and Maria Teresa and I went back to my room to get changed only to find Mummy and Daddy hanging around by my cot. I remember thinking it was odd because they were meant to be having their Chinese instruction class in advance of opening the China Centre Building at Oxford University tomorrow. But then I thought maybe Mummy is feeling better and they want to reassure me things are about to get back to normal.

Oh, George, you fool. It was a trap. I see that now.

They were both looking really weird. And I don't just mean because Mummy was still wearing her Born To Rule onesie and Daddy was smiling in a way that made it look like his face MUST be hurting.

'George,' Daddy said. 'We have news.' There was a pause. Daddy cleared his throat. 'Right,' he said. 'So!' Then he went a bit pink.

'Come on,' Mummy said. 'We haven't got all day. George's History of the Empire class starts in ten minutes.'

Daddy tugged the collar of his shirt uneasily and cleared his throat again. 'Right, so, here we go. Well, George, when you're a grown-up, you get these ... feelings,' he said nervously, 'and they make you want to do things with people that you love. Like Daddy loves Mummy. When you're a grown-up, it's all – ahem – very normal and natural. So, OK, um, what happens is, you might start off by, maybe, holding hands, and then –'

'Stop,' Mummy said, gripping his arm. 'Where is this going?'

'I'm trying to explain, you know ... *the birds and the bees*,' Daddy said, in a quiet voice.

'Why are you telling him about that?' Mummy said, with wide eyes. 'He doesn't need to know that yet. He's one. Bloody hell, Will!'

'Sorry, I thought you said we should explain what's happening,' Daddy said, scratching his head.

'Not HOW it happened,' Mummy said, alarmed. 'For God's sake!'

'Sorry, sorry,' Daddy said. 'I didn't want to tell him – I thought you said we had to.'

Mummy rolled her eyes. 'Georgie,' she said, 'Mummy is having a baby. You're going to be a brother.'

There was a pause. I dribbled a bit. Shock will do that to you.

'How do you think he's taking it?' Daddy asked Mummy.

'I don't know if he understands,' Mummy said.

They got that right. I don't understand. What's wrong with just one child – i.e., me?

'That's why Mummy's been so sick,' Mummy said.

Those peas of deception . . .

'Like I was with you.'

Don't circle this back to me!

'Which is why we're going to announce it tomorrow,' Daddy went on. 'But we wanted to tell you first.'

So I don't have to read it in a newspaper. Apparently this is meant to console me!

'Poor Mummy has been very brave,' Daddy said, rubbing Mummy's back. 'But she's too ill to carry on with her normal schedule. You really are extraordinary, Babykins,' he said to her.

Mummy smiled. 'Well, it's worth it,' she said. 'Look how well this one turned out.' They both beamed at me.

They think I'll be won over by extreme flattery. They can think again. I've already done an entire course to learn how to handle that.

'If the next one is half as wonderful as you, we'll be the two luckiest parents on the planet,' Daddy said, stroking my head. 'We adore you, George.'

Yeah, yeah, yeah. So much, you want to dilute me with some other random baby.

'Heaven knows how this one will live up to your popularity,' Mummy said.

True . . .

'That'll be a job for its team, of course,' Daddy said. 'They start tomorrow.'

Record scratch

ITS TEAM? It's getting its own team already?

'There's a lot to start preparing for,' Mummy said. 'We've got to think about decorating another nursery, about press schedules, wardrobe programmes . . .'

Errrrrr, shall I just move into Lupo's basket or join the Navy on a lifelong tour of the Solomon Islands or something????? I feel like I need a crisis meeting with my team, like, YESTERDAY. How can they not have had intel on this? I don't want to get too distant-relation-Henry VIII, but heads may WELL have to roll.

'There'll be some new courses added to your schedule,' Daddy said brightly. 'Just like there were to mine when I was told Uncle Harry was on his way.'

'And they'll help you prepare for your role as an older brother,' Mummy said, rubbing her stomach.

Media superstar.

Global fashion Titan.

International ambassador for this entire family and nation.

Patron saint of threatened species.

Potential saviour of Scotland.

Heir to the throne.

And now brother. How many roles do these people expect me to fulfil?????

'Mummy and I are both the eldest, just like you,' Daddy said, 'so we know just what you're going through.'

I DOUBT THAT.

'That's right,' Mummy said. 'We know how excited you must be.'

I mean, it's like they'd never met me.

'Being an older brother is totally brilliant,' Daddy said. 'Look how much we all love Uncle Harry.'

'So is being an older sister,' Mummy added. 'Look how much we love Aunt P and Uncle J.'

Well, I suppose they've got a point . . .

'Someone to play with,' Daddy said.

The random baby had better have its own toys. It is well documented that I do NOT share.

'Someone to talk to,' Mummy said.

Talk AT. Everyone knows babies can't talk.

'A best friend for life.' Daddy smiled.

I'll be the judge of that.

'Everyone is very excited,' Mummy said. 'They all think you're going to make the best brother there ever was.'

Wait. 'Everyone is very excited'? They all knew before me??? WHAT IS THIS?

'Even Lupo seems pleased,' Daddy said.

Et tu, Brute?

'I'm sorry if I haven't been the best mummy for the past few weeks,' Mummy said, getting emotional.

Well, what was I supposed to do then? Obviously I had to give her my toy bilby.

Daddy put his arm around her and wiped her eyes with the cuff of his sleeve.

'Babykins,' he said. 'I'm very rarely firm with you – but I'm not having that. You are the best mother in the history of the human race. And that is just a fact.'

'Even though I puked on your Aston Villa T-shirt?' Mummy asked tearfully.

'Even though you puked on my Aston Villa T-shirt,' Daddy said, holding her hand. 'It wasn't a favourite anyway.'

I sat on Mummy's lap and nuzzled into her hair. I

didn't even pull it, just to be nice. Daddy kissed the top of Mummy's head and she leant against his shoulder.

'Everything's going to be OK,' Daddy said.

And then Mummy was sick on his trousers, which did not do much to get that plan off to a good start.

8th September

Well, the cat's out of the bag now, so there's no going back. It's official. This baby is happening.

Its team started today and it's already been given its codename. We all have to refer to it as 'Ringo'. They have chosen Ringo because a) apparently it goes with the name 'George' and b) because it is the name of another famous 'fourth' person and this baby is fourth in line to the throne.

Who are John, Paul, George and Ringo anyway?

Ringo is only the size of a cherry and yet everyone is making the most tremendous fuss about it. Daddy went to Oxford to open that Chinese building on his own today because Mummy is so ill. Why, oh why, did I think it was the peas????? George, it's not like you to be so oblivious, so vacant, so easily fooled. I'm usually one step ahead with these kinds of things. Or so I thought . . .

The press have obviously gone mad. Honestly, you'd think they had nothing else to talk about or that there hadn't been a royal baby before (er, hello???????). Daddy said all people asked him about today were Ringo and Mummy and Mummy's illness. Seriously, shall I just move to the North Pole or live in a tree? He did come back from Oxford with a toy duck for me that someone had given him, so I suppose my public haven't totally forgotten me. Yet.

Uncle Harry is very cheerful about Ringo. He told a journalist that he couldn't be happier to be bumped down the line of succession and that he hopes it's a girl because he thinks it would be hilarious to see Daddy trying to cope with a daughter.

How would ANY of us cope with that? Mummy might because she's a girl too but what am I supposed to do with a girl baby? Will a girl baby expect to play with my football? Or slam the doors that I like slamming? Or splash more than me in the bath? What if the girl baby doesn't like it when I throw things at it, like Cousin Mia? Will I be expected to NOT throw things at it? Ringo is not even here yet and already she needs to buck up her ideas and stop being so sensitive. Even if she turns out to be a boy.

I have so many questions that no one can answer. Mainly because I can't talk that much yet, so I can't ask them. Being one at times like this is tough.

9th September

My Movement Interpreter is now watching me like a hawk. He keeps taking notes and nodding to himself. I want to know what he's writing! Arrrgh! I can't wait until I can read!

Mummy and Daddy came and joined him while I was trying to focus on my art class and started whispering. Tremendously distracting when you're trying to paint a picture of a crocodile driving a tractor.

'How do you think he is?' Mummy asked.

'He's taking the news well, I believe,' the Movement Interpreter said. 'So far, he's chosen to paint with cheerful but gentle colours today, which suggest an upbeat mood.'

I put my hand in the red paint and slammed it onto the paper.

'What an interesting and creative decision, Sir,' my Art Teacher said, nervously spreading a bit more plastic sheeting out on the floor.

'Red . . .' the Movement Interpreter said, writing it down. 'Applied vigorously . . . hmmm.'

'What does it mean?' Daddy asked.

'There may be underlying anger there,' the Movement Interpreter said.

Mummy and Daddy looked at each other.

'Do you think he's angry about Ringo?' Mummy asked.

I knocked over my green paint.

'And potentially jealous,' the Movement Interpreter said, eyeing the green paint and making another note.

'He's already jealous?' Daddy asked anxiously. 'But Ringo isn't even here yet.'

I picked up my paintbrush again and waved it around a bit, flicking paint everywhere, including across my Art Teacher's face as well as my own.

'This is fun, isn't it?' she said, as orange paint dripped from her fringe.

'What do we do?' Daddy asked.

I tried to drink my paint water, but my Art Teacher stopped me. They'll probably let RINGO drink whatever it wants. I can't believe how much Ringo can already get away with. It's incredibly unfair.

'For the time being, we watch and wait,' the Movement Interpreter said. 'This is a process that the Prince may simply need to go through in order to discover what he really feels about Ringo.'

'I know what he needs,' Mummy said, standing up. 'Will someone clean him up, please? And will someone else wipe that orange paint off the Bernini bust.'

Mummy knows me very well. She led me out into the corridor and calmly said, 'Slam away, Georgie. Just let it all out.'

So I ran around and slammed some doors – my favourite thing to do – and shouted and they all watched me, but I didn't care.

I'm exhausted now. It doesn't change the fact that Ringo the Usurper will be here by spring, but I do feel better.

10th September

Lest we forget that it's not ALL about Ringo, Uncle Harry officially opened the Invictus Games at the Olympic Stadium today. Goonie, GaGa and Daddy went along to listen to him do his speech and, thanks to Mummy, he didn't read the one about the rhinos. It's not difficult to get confused when you've got so many speeches to give, like they all do. Uncle Harry has been excited about these games for ages. So excited he doesn't even mind that there won't be any rhinos there.

Mummy didn't go because she's still feeling so ill and they sent David along in my place, because I still don't feel I can really leave her while she's like this. He does quite a lot of cover work for me. Mummy cleared our schedules for the afternoon and we lay on the sofa together and watched a thing called *Keeping Up with the Kardashians*. The main story is about a lot of sisters with dark hair who eat salad out of plastic bowls and look at their phones.

'Yay, I love this episode,' Mummy said, while I played with my bricks. 'It's when Bruce and Kris were still together and Kim still had her old nose.'

They showed one episode after another and we watched all of them.

'Jonathan is being so shady,' Mummy said, shaking her head. 'He can't just go off wine-tasting in Sonoma with Kris and lie about it to Kim.'

I fiddled around with the remote and pressed things, then tried to call Daddy on it because it does look a bit like a phone and I wanted to find out how the Invictus Games were going.

'Give the remote to Mummy,' Mummy said. 'I must remember to talk to your Class Co-ordinator about when you start your digital equipment course . . .'

By this point in the programme, the short sister was sitting on the floor of a cupboard where she casually announced she was having a baby. It's contagious!

'Poor Kourt,' Mummy said. 'The Lord is being such a freak about this. I know he's had a tough summer since Jeff and Bonnie died, but he needs to stop getting slashed up in Vegas and sort himself out.'

I looked at the Kourt one. She seemed fine to me. Her expression didn't change once – she just sort of shrugged her shoulders. This programme is brilliant.

'WHEN is Kim and Kanye's super-mansion going to be finished?' Mummy went on. 'They can't keep camping at the Jenner house. North needs her own room.'

Then we snuggled on the sofa and went to sleep until it got so hot under Mummy's hair that it woke me up.

When Daddy, Uncle Harry, Goonie and GaGa got back, they were all SO EXCITED. Uncle Harry was literally jumping up and down and Daddy said he gave a brilliant speech and Goonie and GaGa said they were very proud of him. Mummy clapped weakly from the sofa and Uncle Harry looked a bit sad.

'That's it. I'm cancelling my birthday party,' he said.

'No,' Mummy whimpered. 'I'm so much better.'

Uncle Harry sat down on the sofa. 'No offence, Vomiting Valerie, but I don't want you there in this state. And if you're not there, I don't want to be there either.'

'Spike's right,' Daddy said. 'It's not a party without you.'

'Who would destroy me during the vodka ice sculpture challenge?' Uncle Harry said.

'Who would make me dance to On Reflection?' Daddy said.

'One Direction,' Mummy said.

'Them as well,' Daddy said.

'Who would dare us to take all our clothes off and then photograph us holding strategically placed Fabergé eggs?' Uncle Harry said.

GaGa roared with laughter. 'I want a copy of that,' she said.

'Or make us perform a seance to contact the spirit of Great Aunt Margaret?' Daddy said.

'Good grief, I hope you didn't,' Goonie said. 'You wake Aunt Margs at your peril, no matter what life plane she's currently making her way through sixty Chesterfields a day on.'

'So we gathered . . .' Uncle Harry said. 'The point is, Val, I'm not turning thirty without my best mate and her sick bowl by my side.'

'That actually makes me feel really emotional.' Daddy's eyes glistened. 'You guys.'

GaGa laughed again. 'Put your umbrellas up, this pipe's going to burst!' she hooted. 'Sweet old sensitive thing.'

Mummy smiled at Daddy and Uncle Harry. 'You're both pathetic, obviously.'

'That's settled then,' Uncle Harry said. 'Now hurry up and get better. This whole pregnancy thing is immensely inconvenient.'

'Poor you,' Mummy said, raising an eyebrow. 'I'm so sorry.'

'So you should be,' Uncle Harry said. 'And so should you.' He pointed at Daddy. Daddy went a bit pink.

What everyone is failing to verbalize is that it is Ringo who has ruined Uncle Harry's thirtieth birthday party, which was meant to be happening tomorrow night. Yet another example of its perpetual thoughtlessness.

'Look, I'll allow you to postpone for two days, but that's it,' Mummy said.

'Fine,' Uncle Harry said. 'Gives me extra time to work on my special birthday dance routine, which I shall be performing solo before the speeches.'

Then they did their funny handclapping rhyme and Daddy just watched admiringly, even though he still doesn't know how to do it.

The party has now been rescheduled to Thursday. Mummy's doctors have said she might be better by then, so everyone is feeling hopeful. Uncle Harry says he's going to wear a party hat and nothing else, and from the look on Daddy's face when he said it, I don't think he was joking.

15th September

Happy birthday, Uncle Harry! He is THIRTY today!!!!!! Someone oil those joints!

He came into my room this morning wearing a hat with two cans of beer on either side of his head that had a straw coming from each one, shouting, 'Happy birthday to me!' It was so much fun, particularly when I helped him open his presents. Mummy and Daddy gave him lots of different things, including a new wallet with his initials on it so he has something to carry around the £10 million he inherits today.

My own present was a painting I did for him in my art class. It's kind of an abstract piece – mostly orange, like his hair. With a few streaks of purple that I did with my hands. He said it was really awesome and would be going on his fridge immediately. Next to the photo of Usain Colt signed by Usain Bolt.

17th September

Uncle Harry's party has been rescheduled for tonight, but Mummy is still not better. Daddy and Uncle Harry are so upset, but Mummy has insisted they go ahead. I think the reason I'm not going is because someone needs to stay with Mummy. And I don't want to over-shadow Uncle Harry – it is his evening, after all.

Mummy keeps reminding Daddy that he will be there representing both of them and has therefore made him swear he'll 'get on it like Sonic', whatever that means. Goonie and GaGa have gone to Scotland to escape the party, which is being held at Clarence House. That is the house where they claimed to have contacted Great Great Aunt Margaret in a seance and she told them about her secret Famous Grouse cup-board behind the 1961 Graham Sutherland portrait of Great Great Granny in the Morning Room.

Daddy read me my story in black tie tonight. He asked me if he could have some of my milk because apparently it's good lining for your stomach, so he swigged it out of my bottle when I didn't want any more. He looked a bit nervous, actually. Uncle Harry's parties can sometimes be 'like *Total Wipeout* meets

Hieronymus Bosch,' Daddy says. Is that good or bad? I wonder if they'll play Pass the Castle like we did at my birthday party.

Tomorrow is when the people in Scotland decide the thing they're supposed to be deciding. I hope for GG's sake that the thing they decide is what GG wants because she is not sleeping a wink at the moment. She was telling David about it last week – but in the voice of someone called Sean Connery and apparently it was not only very funny, but also very accurate. It's important to still laugh even when things are serious.

18th September

So the party seems like it was a total disaster because they are all feeling terrible today. It's so sad. Uncle Harry looks like he slept in a tree (I think he did, actually) and Daddy is being sick like Mummy. Mummy said she is so gagged out by Daddy being sick that it's making her want to be more sick. The three of them spent the day crawling around the house complaining that they didn't feel well. Uncle Harry said he feels like someone is trying to break out of his head with a fork.

Uncle Harry now has only one eyebrow and various different birthday messages written all over his body in ink that won't come off. They've been playing this funny game where Mummy reads a girl's name from the guest list and Daddy tries to help Uncle Harry match the message to the name.

Apparently they all ended up in Great Great Aunt Margaret's old apartments jumping on the beds, dressed in some of her ancient silk dressing-gowns and throwing one of the Fabergé eggs around like a rugby ball. It sounds like a pretty good party to me – I don't know why they're clutching their heads and groaning so much today as if it had been the worst evening of all time.

Also Uncle Harry says his phone wiped all his contacts when someone dropped it in a bath that had been filled with beer. This has proved to be rather awkward because LOTS of girls have rung him today, presumably to say happy birthday again and thank you for the lovely party. Every time he answered, Mummy and Daddy started laughing because he kept having to guess who he was talking to. He called one girl Millie when her name was Mary and another one Ella when her name was Florence. And he kept saying things like, 'Of course I remember, babes,' and 'it meant a lot to me too,' and 'if I said I'd take you whale-watching in the Antarctic Peninsula, then, then, then I *will*,' all the while making an anxious face at Mummy and Daddy and mouthing what looked like 'HELP ME.'

In other news, Daddy rang GG today to see if she is OK. They had quite a long conversation and it ended with Daddy and Uncle Harry shouting a song in the most bizarre accent about walking five hundred miles (Mummy had to tell me because you could NOT have worked that out yourself) down the phone while they jumped up and down to cheer her up. I could hear her laughing her head off – even the Mean Girls started barking.

I feel a bit guilty about not wearing the kilt now. I wonder if Scotland has any endangered species they'd like me to bring global recognition to? I seem to remember someone once saying something about a monster that is very shy and only makes an appearance once in a while. I mean, if they want me to be photographed with it, I'd be up for that.

19th September

Scotland has not done the thing GG didn't want them to do. I know this because pipers played 'Scotland The Brave' this morning to wake me up. It was startling and stirring in equal measure. GG is very happy and says we get to keep our flag. G-Pop and Goonie are happy because they get to keep their skirts.

20th September

Daddy has gone to Malta instead of Mummy, who is too ill to travel, to help them commemorate fifty years of independence. Today we mostly ate Maltesers because we are having Maltese week to support Daddy.

'I'll just have tea,' David said in today's meeting with GG. 'I'm not that hungry.'

GG looked surprised. 'Of course,' she said.

David and GG had some tea poured out for them.

'I'm so relieved about Scotland, Prime Minister,' GG said.

'Yes, Scotland,' David said, eyeing the tea tray. 'Big relief. Oh look, that honey is labelled from the Balmoral estate. What a nice touch.' He picked up the honey from the tray.

'Yes, we've been making it for years,' GG said.

'Well, maybe just one piece of toast with this lovely honey,' he said. 'Only because we're talking about Scotland.'

'Indeed,' GG said.

David picked up two pieces of toast.

'Gosh, this is delicious. Can I make one for you, Ma'am?' he said to GG.

'No, thank you,' GG said. 'Back to Scotland – what is your next move?'

'Perhaps some of the shortbread,' David said, wiping his hands on a napkin. 'Seeing as we're celebrating Scotland staying in the union and everything.'

'Do help yourself . . .' GG said. But David was already tucking into a large piece of shortbread.

'I might keep one for later, if that's all right?' he said. 'I just get so peckish in the afternoons.'

I offered him some of the Mean Girls' dog chocs, too. He respectfully declined – but not until he'd given it quite a lot of thought.

22nd September

We have just finished Skyping Daddy in Malta. He said he is having a lovely time and that he went to visit a centre for teenagers where he played table football. I'm so jealous!!!

'I scored two goals!' Daddy said. 'It was classic bantz.'

'Errrr . . .' Mummy said. 'Please tell me you didn't say that out loud.'

'I did, actually. Because I am peng,' Daddy said. 'True dat.'

Mummy put her head in her hands. 'Oh God.'

'What?' Daddy asked. 'Is that wrong?'

23rd September

Malta has seen a 71 per cent increase in the number of people interested in going there on holiday because of Daddy's visit. I'm glad some of 'the George Effect' is rubbing off on him. He's got to make up 29 per cent to get to my level, but it's a start.

26th September

Mummy is looking a little bit less green, these days. She has had a wardrobe meeting to plan her pregnancy-outfit strategy and her Hair Team are working on the plan to cope with her hair thickening because of Ringo. Apparently with me she ended up having to wear a discreet neck brace because it became so heavy.

29th September

What if Ringo has hair like Mummy and I have hair like Daddy? Arrrggh!!!

October 2014

5th October

A thing called *Homeland* started today. Mummy and Daddy wouldn't stop talking about it.

'What are we going to do about *Downton*?' Daddy asked. 'They're on at the same time.'

'We're recording them both,' Mummy said, 'because this is the modern age.'

'But which one do we watch first?' Daddy asked.

'We watch *Homeland*,' Mummy said. 'Like, obvs.'

'But what if Lord Grantham –'

'William,' Mummy said calmly, 'that sounds like the beginning of a sentence laced with challenge and riddled with defiance.'

'Never,' Daddy said.

'But just so we're clear. Who comes first? Your wife or Hugh Bonneville?'

'My completely adorable and perfect wife,' Daddy said.

'Correct. Now, go and get me some ice to eat before I change my mind about giving you a Chinese burn.'

'I'm not here, you can't see me,' Daddy said, running off.

'Chop! Chop!' Mummy shouted after him.

I've never seen a human being look happier than Daddy as he sprinted out of the door.

10th October

I went to play at GG's again today. The Mean Girls were on their best behaviour because of someone called Angelina Jolie. GG gave her the Insignia of an Honorary Dame Grand Cross of the Most Distinguished Order of St Michael and St George. That long name, and it's just two stars with a bow in a box. She seemed to like it, though.

Angelina and GG talked about what it's like to have a big family, and when the photographer was gone, I went and sat on Angelina's lap for a bit. She has enormous eyes and an enormous mouth and a tiny nose. I couldn't help just sort of staring at her because she is REALLY pretty and she smells like Goonie's flower meadow.

'I miss my kids being this age, don't you, Ma'am?' Angelina said to GG, smiling at me like a big, beautiful moon.

'Err . . .' GG replied.

Then Angelina's family came in. Her husband is

called Brad. I'm really hoping he didn't notice how much GG was staring at him. Brad and Angelina's children are all so shiny and perfect that they look like they were made on a computer. Apparently they are all home-schooled and they travel the world a lot. There are loads of them and they all curtsied and bowed to GG. Then she asked them if they liked London.

'Yes, thank you, Your Majesty,' the one called Zahara said. 'This noble Titan of the Grande Dame that is Europe is both provocative and charming.'

GG asked the one called Pax what he liked best so far.

'I am enjoying the cultural diversity of this fair city,' he said. 'It has Hanoi's mystery, Rome's gravitas and New York's sense of possibility.'

I went to go and look at the two blond twins. I prodded one of them to make sure they weren't dolls.

'Thank you for welcoming us to your home,' the one called Vivienne said. 'We are grateful for, and humbled by, your hospitality.'

'Yes,' Brad said. 'Isn't it wonderful to see the internal configurations of how this nation's premier family works? We'll be discussing it as a topic over dinner later.'

'I just feel so blessed,' the one called Knox said. 'This is an almost ineffable experience.'

'But one that will surely render a eucatastrophe,' the one called Shiloh said.

'The desire to gasconade to our peers about this is going to prove very challenging,' the one called Maddox said, 'were it not for its didactic elements, which are sure to prevail.'

They all nodded in agreement.

People keep saying that American is the same as English, but it really isn't.

14th October

Mummy and Daddy's lives continue to be ruled by TV. A thing called *The Apprentice* starts tonight. It's all they've talked about all day.

'I'm a winner!' Daddy said. 'There's no *I* in "team", but there are five in "individual brilliance".'

'You're not a bloody winner! You lost!' Mummy said.

'You're a total shambles. You're fired!' Daddy said.

'You haven't got a clue. Not a bloody clue!' Mummy said.

'You're fired again!' Daddy said.

'No, YOU'RE fired!' Mummy said.

'You can't fire me, I'm Lord Sugar!' Daddy said.

'No, I'M Lord Sugar,' Mummy said. 'Get your blatantly empty wheelie-case and get in that bloody cab!'

'I'm not giving up on my dream of being a businessman! One day I will rule the world!'

'Not any more,' Mummy said. 'You're only going to rule a tiny bit of it!'

And then they both had hysterics.

It went on like this all day. I was actually relieved to have to get back to my Chaucer studies and that's saying something.

18th October

We had lunch with GG and G-Pop at HQ today. It was cold lobster and salad, and some wine from a dusty bottle for everyone except GG, who prefers a gin and Dubonnet.

'What the hell is this?' G-Pop said, piercing a radish on his fork. 'Do I look like I live in a hutch?'

'Don't answer that,' Daddy said, very quietly, to Uncle Harry.

'I just want a bloody decent lunch for once. Sick to the back teeth of this fancy stuff,' G-Pop said, throwing his fork down. 'What is this we're drinking? Something bottled by Harald Hardrada in the eleventh century for an "Up Yours, Godwinson" party? I just want an honest pint of John Smith's, Lilibet.'

'Well, don't look at me,' GG said. 'I shan't stop you.'

'Can't a man just have a pork pie and a beer if he wants it,' G-Pop grumbled, 'instead of these endless plates of frilly bloody knickers?'

Uncle Harry started sniggering so badly that he had to put most of his napkin in his mouth and that set Mummy and Daddy off.

The Mean Girls were swanning around like they ruled the world, barking and begging for food. They growled at us, but rolled over on their backs for GG. Typical.

'Who's a clever girl?' GG said, as she leant down to rub Candy's chest. 'Who was very good and only bit the Deputy Yeoman once this morning?'

Candy licked GG's hand, whimpering and fawning, then shooting us a death stare. Vulcan was all gang-leader as usual, leading the other dogs around and barking at the footmen. Holly and Willow are such a pair of sheep! Vulcan isn't even a Corgi, he's a Dorgi, and STILL they bow to him.

Uncle Harry made a point of requesting some beer for G-Pop to butter him up before putting me on his lap as a human shield and finally going ahead with his dare to ask G-Pop whether he'd wear tusks for Tuskcember.

'It's George's idea, so if you're going to be angry, you should be angry with him,' Uncle Harry said. 'I'm only asking you on his behalf, it's nothing to do with me.'

'Are you mad?' G-Pop shouted.

'Stop wriggling,' Uncle Harry whispered to me, 'I need to make sure you're covering all my major organs.'

G-Pop said he would quite frankly rather listen to a

Tom Jones record on repeat for the rest of his life, even though he's a 'bloody awful singer' who 'sounds like he gargles with pebbles' and 'sings the most hideous songs'. And then GG briefly sang something about it not being unusual to be loved by anyone in a very loud, deep voice that was apparently extremely accurate.

This means Mummy has lost the bet because Uncle Harry was so brave. Which also means she has to start thinking of horse words to sneak into her next conversation with Great Aunt Annie.

'What about "We still have to giddy-up at least twice in the night for George"?' she asked Daddy. 'Can I get away with that?'

21st October

We are having Singapore Week at home because the President of Singapore and his wife, Mrs Tan, are visiting London at the moment. Mummy and Daddy met them today.

Mummy gets so tired because of Ringo that she has been struggling to stay awake when she's working. Fortunately GG has taught her how to fall asleep with her eyes open, like a prawn – a trick that's been passed down through the generations. Mummy is thrilled to have mastered it. She says she has no recollection of the entire day, but you'd never tell from the pictures.

GG had a party for the President and his wife this evening at HQ, but Mummy and Daddy didn't go. Instead we had Hainanese Chicken Rice, Laksa and Sambal and Nasi Lemak for supper in their honour. Mummy didn't have any prawns, though, as she has a new-found respect for them.

24th October

GG sent her first tweet today!

I'm obviously highly aware of Twitter, which I understand is a place where people get together online to talk about me and sometimes other things.

GG's tweet said, 'It is a pleasure to open the Information Age exhibition today at the @ScienceMuseum and I hope people will enjoy visiting. Elizabeth R.'

So far it has been retweeted 37,000 times.

'Is that good or bad?' GG asked Daddy on the phone later.

'I have no idea,' Daddy said. 'I'll ask George – he knows more about this stuff than I do.'

28th October

From Twitter to Twitching. G-Pop went to a reception for the British Trust of Ornithology today because he is a twitcher. Apparently he wanted to wear the T-shirt Uncle Harry had made for him that says 'Kill a cat and save a bird' but GG said he wasn't allowed.

31st October

Today is Hallowe'en. I spent it dressed as a terrifying skeleton. We saw Grandpa M, who changed four times because he couldn't decide which costume he liked best. First he was a mad scientist, then he was a creepy clown, then he was a sexy cat and then he was someone called Jeremy Clarkson. Everyone said the last one was the scariest.

November 2014

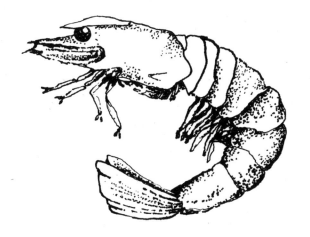

2nd November

Ringo's team asked for a meeting with my team today. We sat in the media conference room – my team on one side, Ringo's team on the other. I was Chair. Which means I sat in a chair at the top of the table and threw pens.

'We love the work you've done so far with Prince George,' Ringo's head of Global Strategy said, 'and we want to imitate it as much as possible. We're here to learn.'

'Yes,' Ringo's Media Manager said. 'We bow to your superior knowledge. 'The George Effect' is a real template for the kind of global domination we want to achieve with Ringo.'

My Press Secretary eyed his counterpart across the table.

'I think the likelihood of you being able to replicate what the Prince has achieved is an ambition you should, respectfully, contain,' he said.

'There is only one Prince George,' my head of Global Strategy said icily.

Both sides glared at each other.

'Of course,' Ringo's Press Secretary said. 'Nobody is suggesting a copycat strategy – but it's unlikely we'll need one.'

'Especially if Ringo turns out to be a girl,' Ringo's head of Global Strategy said provocatively.

'A girl with her mother's good looks,' Ringo's Make-up Artist said.

'And her mother's sense of style,' Ringo's stylist said.

'And her mother's hair,' Ringo's Hairdresser said.

'A boy would work just as well,' Ringo's Press Secretary said. 'An insanely popular second son by the name of Prince Harry springs to mind.'

'To be honest, this is more a courtesy meeting than anything else,' Ringo's Media Manager said. 'We actually have plans in place.'

'You'll need them,' my head of Global Strategy said archly.

Then the meeting was adjourned.

'I don't want to use the word "competition",' my Press Secretary said afterwards, 'but they started it.'

'There is no competition,' my head of Global Strategy said, 'because you can't compete with a phenomenon.'

They both looked at me.

You have to admit, he's got a point.

3rd November

I found Mummy in the kitchen today sitting on the floor by the fridge. She was drinking straight from a large container of milk. 'Do you know?' she said, with a milk moustache. 'I can't get enough of this milk. I love it. I want to marry it.'

Daddy came in and looked a bit scared. 'Golly,' he said. 'This is new.'

'More milk,' was all Mummy said, shutting her eyes and continuing to down it furiously.

7th November

Mini fridges full of milk have been put into every room in case Mummy gets a craving. I'm a fan of milk myself, so I can see where she's coming from.

Having said that, I'm making sure I grip the bottles for dear life when I have my milk in case she gets any ideas.

12th November

Mummy did a test at the GSK Human Performance lab she visited today. She had to tap a big screen with colours on it to prove her brain is still working. Fortunately, it is (no thanks to Ringo). She loved it, of course. Being brilliant at everything makes this kind of thing quite a lot of fun.

'I told them I wished you'd been there to do the test with me,' she said to Daddy. 'Because I would have kicked your sorry little royal arse.'

Daddy looked at me with a massive smile. 'That's my girl,' he said. 'She's back.'

13th November

Mummy and Daddy are going to the *Royal Variety Performance* tonight. Usually GG has to go, which is fine because she does her prawn trick, but she asked Mummy and Daddy to go in her place this year. One of Mummy's favourite bands, One Direction, is part of the line-up, so she had to try really hard not to scream when GG rang.

'Who's your favourite?' Mummy asked Daddy over lunch.

'I like Wayne,' he said.

'Zayn,' Mummy said.

'Yes, him too.'

'Guess who my favourite is?' Mummy said.

'Leo?'

'Liam – no.'

'Gary?'

'He's in Take That.'

Daddy thought for a bit.

'I know!' he said. 'Barry!'

'Harry,' Mummy said. 'Correct.'

'Yes, I like him too,' Daddy said. 'Good singer.'

'As if that mattered,' Mummy said. 'He's hot.'

'I like that song they did – what's it called again, Babykins? "Never Ending Story"?'

' "Story of My Life".'

'Good song, anyway,' Daddy said. 'Love that song.'

Then they were briefed on who was going to be there.

'Lord Lloyd Webber,' Mummy read aloud. 'Try saying that after downing a pint and spinning round five times.'

Then Mummy's Hair Team came in.

'What are we thinking for tonight's look?' Mummy's Hair Stylist asked.

'I think put it up and out of the way,' Mummy said. 'We need One Direction to stay focused for their performance.'

'By the way, what should I talk to them about tonight, Babykins?' Daddy asked.

'Just tell them you've been following their progress closely,' Mummy said.

'Have I been following their progress closely?' Daddy asked.

'Whatever – just make sure I get my photo taken with Harry,' Mummy said.

'OK,' Daddy said. 'And I'll go for one with Barry.'

Mummy didn't even bother to reply.

14th November

Happy birthday, Goonie! He is SIXTY-SIX today!!!! That's almost two whole Daddys!

Uncle Harry came over this morning to find out the goss on the *Royal Variety Performance.*

'I sort of met One Direction once,' Uncle Harry said. 'They carried a cardboard cut-out of me on stage during the Radio 1 Teen Awards a couple of years ago.'

'Louis's hair . . .' Daddy said, bewitched. 'Did you see it? How does he make it stand up like that? How?'

'Do you remember Jack Whitehall from school?' Uncle Harry asked Mummy. 'He's always making gags about you being the one that got away.'

'Good to know I've got options,' Mummy said.

17th November

When we went swimming at HQ today we bumped into G-Pop on our way to the pool.

'What's all that inflatable stuff you're carrying?' he asked Mummy.

'It's George's armbands,' Mummy said.

'Armbands? Can't he swim yet?' G-Pop sounded surprised.

'Well, no, not on his own,' Mummy said.

'I was diving for sponges at his age,' G-Pop said. 'What's the matter with him? Scared of the water or something?'

'No, he loves it – but he's also only sixteen months.'

'Throw him in at the deep end and let him fend for himself. It's the only way they learn,' G-Pop said. 'What my father did with me and it didn't do me any harm.'

Mummy didn't say anything.

'Apart from the drowning incident. But they brought me round eventually and there was no permanent damage. That was the main thing.'

'OK,' Mummy said.

'Ended up a Commander in the Royal Navy,' G-Pop said. 'And I didn't use a rubber ring to get me there.'

'I believe you,' Mummy said.

'You'll be telling me he doesn't know how to play cricket next,' G-Pop said.

'He absolutely does,' Mummy lied.

'Glad to hear it,' G-Pop said. 'Scored his first century yet?'

'Yes,' Mummy lied again.

20th November

I could at least play cricket with Ringo. Just a thought.

23rd November

Ringo better not be better at cricket than me.

26th November

Mummy and Daddy were totally hysterical today because Daddy gave someone called Damian Lewis an OBE at HQ. He used to be in *Homeland*, one of the many TV shows they are obsessed with.

'Two words,' Mummy said. 'Hot ginger.'

'Even I think he's a hot ginger,' Daddy said.

'Even Spike thinks he's a hot ginger,' Mummy said.

'Shall I try and find out if Brody really is coming back?' Daddy asked.

'Yes! I mean no!' Mummy said, biting her lip. 'OK, no, don't – except yes, because we need to know!'

'OK, I'll do everything I can,' Daddy said. 'But you know how secretive these TV people are.'

'OK, wait, wait, wait – don't ask him,' Mummy said.

'Except, no, definitely ask him. We can't be expected to wait until Sunday to find out.'

'OK, I totally will,' Daddy said. 'I can't believe I'm going to meet Brody! This is so cool!'

When Daddy came back from the investiture, Mummy made him act out exactly what had happened.

'OK, you be me and I'll be Damian Lewis,' Daddy said.

'OK, OK,' Mummy said excitedly. 'Hello, Damian Lewis.'

'Hello, Sir,' Daddy said, shaking Mummy's hand.

'No, no – please call me William,' Mummy said. 'Or even Wombat because that's what my family call me. Guess what? We went to the same school and I'm your biggest fan.'

'I didn't actually say that, but –'

'In fact, I am thinking of making you godfather to my new baby because I think you're such a legend,' Mummy interrupted. 'I have a man-crush on you – and my wife has an actual crush on you.'

'Right, this isn't –'

'Between you and me, this OBE is fine, but we both know a knighthood is the one everyone really cares about,' Mummy said, suddenly lowering her voice. 'I can make that happen for you without you having to wait until you're eighty.'

'Really?' Daddy said.

'Of course. I know people who know people – know

what I'm saying?' Mummy said, tapping the side of her nose and winking. 'All it would take is a word in Granny's ear and it's "Arise, Sir Damian."'

'I like the sound of that,' Daddy said.

'I only need one little tiny minuscule favour,' Mummy said.

'What's that?'

'Just tell me if Brody's coming back?' Mummy said. 'One very simple, very small question.'

'Right,' Daddy said. 'Can't do that.'

Mummy's face fell. 'Oh,' she said, stepping back from him. 'Why not?'

'I'm contractually not allowed to talk about plot lines,' Daddy said.

'Are you sure about that, maybe-godfather-to-a-royal-baby?' Mummy said.

'I'm afraid so,' Daddy said.

'And there's nothing I can do to persuade you otherwise?' Mummy said.

'Nope.'

'That is disappointing,' Mummy said. 'I'm afraid you leave me no choice. Guards? Arrest this ginger.'

'What? Where are you taking me?' Daddy said, sounding shocked.

'That's classified,' Mummy said.

'But you can't do this – I'm Damian Lewis,' Daddy said.

'I think you'll find I can,' Mummy said. 'And this conversation is over. Along with your career.'

There was a pause.

'OK, that's not actually what happened,' Daddy said.

'Did he tell you?' Mummy asked.

'No.'

'Did you even ask him?'

'No.'

'Well, then, it should have been what happened,' Mummy said. 'If I held investitures, we'd get the results we want.'

'We did talk about school, though,' Daddy said.

'That doesn't help me,' Mummy said. 'Now we have to wait. And you know how much I don't like to be kept waiting.'

Daddy went a bit pink. 'I'll call Granny now and ask to have him arrested and confined until he talks,' he said.

'Better,' Mummy said.

Sometimes I think Mummy and Daddy watch too much TV.

27th November

So my team have an interesting proposition for me. They want me to spearhead a campaign to make Christmas Cheer the official mood of the nation next month. This will involve me doing a photo shoot to thank the press for not taking pictures of me on a day when I'm not in the mood. My Wardrobe Team have been working on a strategy for this over the past month.

They presented me with the following outfit: white shirt, navy shorts, navy socks (long), navy shoes, navy tank top. With an embroidered bumblebee on it.

We were doing fine until the bee. I mean, just no.

And yet: how to communicate this when you can't talk that much?

I thumped my fists on the table. My Movement Interpreter sat up.

'Wait,' he said. 'The Prince is trying to tell us something.'

I wriggled in my chair and started to complain a bit.

'Get him out!' someone shouted.

I was taken out of my chair.

'We're listening, Sir,' my Mood Analyst said. 'Show us.'

It wasn't obvious at first what the alternative should be, but my initial thought was 'go traditional'. So I marched.

'What's he doing?' my Mood Analyst said. 'Is it a robot?'

Robot, for goodness' sake. These people.

I growled – like a bear. As in bearskin. Surely that's incredibly obvious.

'Tigers!' my stylist said. 'That could work?'

I mean, if I'd meant tiger, I would have done a tiger growl. As soon as I can talk, I'm having every one of my team do a course with my Zoologist on animal sounds. The ignorance.

Sometimes, though, you have to let people catch up with you. So I picked up one of my toy soldiers and threw it.

'Soldiers!' they all shouted. 'It's genius!'

Give me strength. At least we got there in the end.

28th November

My Christmas Cheer campaign shoot was today in the courtyard. Daddy's Private Secretary took the photos.

It was cold, but I shunned a coat. It's what the professionals do.

The outfit should prove to be a success. That 'George' cashmere jumper shifted over a thousand units in four days after I wore it for the shoot with Lupo, Mummy and Daddy, so hopefully this one will go the same way. Ringo has got its work cut out if it wants to compete against this style colossus.

29th November

A weird thing happened today. They gave me a baby. Not a real one, a plastic one – so obviously I threw it up in the air, then dragged it around by one of its legs, before sucking its nose and then I put it in Lupo's basket. Lupo didn't seem too happy about that and got its arm in his mouth, shaking it and growling. I thought it was funny, but no one else seemed to. They all looked at each other and started making notes. Especially when I lobbed the plastic baby down the stairs and laughed.

30th November

There has been a change to my schedule. I am now doing a course called 'Sibling Rivalry'. The plastic baby is doing it with me. It sat on a plastic chair next to me and stared straight ahead with its plastic eyes.

The good thing was, there were lots of toys in the room for me to play with. No need to even look at the plastic baby. Plenty of other stuff to get on with.

I was zooming around with a cool ambulance that had flashing blue lights and a siren, thinking everything was fine, when my Sibling Rivalry Coach came and sat down next to me. Bringing the plastic baby.

'Hello, George,' he said. 'This is Ringo.' He waved the plastic baby at me.

'You look like you're having fun with that ambulance. Maybe Ringo could have a go.'

I grabbed hold of the ambulance as tightly as I could.

If Ringo wants this ambulance, it's going to have to fight me for it, I thought.

'Whenever you're ready,' he said calmly.

How about NEVER?

'Don't be sad, Ringo. George just really likes that ambulance,' he said to the fake Ringo.

Ringo didn't look sad. It looked exactly the same. I do have actual eyes. Ones that aren't made of plastic, unlike some people around here.

'OK, George,' my Sibling Rivalry Coach said calmly. 'Ringo understands that you want to play with the ambulance and that's OK. Another thing that's OK is sharing your toys, but we can leave that for today.'

Of all the toys in the room, Ringo wants to play with mine and apparently I'm the one with the problem. I mean, who are these people?

December 2014

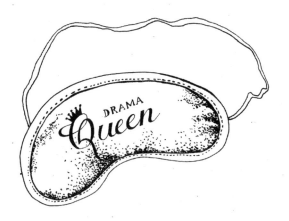

1st December

This morning I was woken by the choir singing 'All I Want For Christmas Is You' because it is DECEMBER. December is an important time of year. A baby called Jesus was born and everyone gets presents on his birthday, not just him.

Anyway, I'm doing Jesus classes now because one day I will be Defender of the Faith and Supreme Governor of the Church of England. I will get to give archbishops jobs and let priests swear oaths to me. Jesus came into this world to be king too, apparently, but he didn't get a crocodile when he was born. He only got a lamb and some stuff in pots. Poor Jesus.

They have put an ENORMOUS tree up in our house and we have carol singers singing next to it all the time. It's so cheerful. My Present Team are being looked after by the coaches, nutritionists and psychologists from Team GB so they can cope with this extra-busy period. I saw them being taken on a run this morning and they're all drinking this weird green juice to keep their stamina up.

It's going to be a very good month.

3rd December

'I know we're only three days in,' David said in his meeting with GG today, 'but I'm already finding the Christmas period murder on the waistline.'

I watched him push a sandwich around on his plate, picking it up and then putting it down again.

'Please don't feel obligated to eat anything,' GG said. 'Tea is provided as a courtesy more than anything else.'

'Right, right . . .' David said, pursing his lips, his smooth skin glowing. 'I suppose it's fine to have *one* though, isn't it?'

'I think so,' GG said supportively.

'Well, if you insist,' David said, munching down the sandwich. 'I say, is that a crumpet?'

'Yes, but don't feel –' GG started to say. But David was already eating the crumpet.

'Bliss,' he said, shutting his eyes.

'And now, Prime Minister,' GG said, 'perhaps we can return to the EU?'

'Of course,' David said. 'You have the lemon biscuit. That's one thing I AM going to force myself to leave.'

5th December

Who is Father Christmas by the way and how does he know all this stuff about me? When I refused to eat the stupid kale and threw it on the floor, Maria Teresa said Father Christmas would know and I might go on the Naughty List. Well, hear this, Father Christmas – I too have a list of my own. It's called 'People Who Will Never Get Knighthoods'. You've been warned.

6th December

Today we had lunch at HQ because GG had a question to ask everyone.

'We're going to start work on my Christmas speech soon,' she announced to the table. 'Does anyone have any suggestions for what I should talk about?'

'I do,' Uncle Harry said. 'And I'm glad you've raised this, actually, Lilibet, because it's been bothering me for some time.'

'Go on,' GG said.

'Is the Christmas number one really going to be an *X Factor* winner again this year? And if so, what does this say about us as a nation?'

'Not quite what I had in mind, but . . .' GG said. 'Anyone else?'

'I've got something, Mummy,' Goonie said. 'Are we showing enough appreciation for our gardens? Are we taking the time to check in with them every morning after they've spent a cold night outside? It's terribly important that as a society, we make the effort to really connect with our natural surroundings, to talk to our plants.'

'Hmmm . . .' GG said. 'And what about you, Camilla?'

'How about a joke this year?' GaGa said. 'I always think a speech should have a few laughs in it. You could do the one about two nuns in a bath. That always goes down well.'

'Yes,' GG said brightly. 'That is a good one.'

'If it's jokes you want,' G-Pop said, 'why don't you talk about me having to eat these so called "Hand-Dived Scallops" when I specifically asked for a Scotch egg, because that is a bloody joke.'

'You could mention how pleased we are that Lady Edith seems to be heading towards happiness in *Downton* now that she can finally be a mother to Marigold,' Daddy said. 'It's been very unifying for the country.'

'Or how important it is to support the arts,' Mummy said. 'We need to show One Direction that we appreciate all their hard work.'

'Well, this has all been terribly useful,' GG said. 'And I shall make a note of all of it.'

GG is not going to make a note of any of it.

7th December

We are having America Week because Mummy and Daddy are about to go to New York. Mummy is all over the hot dogs like a rash.

8th December

YO.

That's the American for 'Hello'. Mummy and Daddy are in New York. I wore a Statue of Liberty foam crown for our Skype call and a T-shirt that says 'I'm a Carrie' but I didn't know what that meant.

9th December

Mummy said on the call today that she visited a centre yesterday where the children all thought she was Elsa from *Frozen*. Odd, because (a) Elsa has white hair and Mummy has brown hair, (b) Elsa is Queen of Arendelle and Mummy is only Princess of the United Kingdom and (c) Elsa doesn't play hockey and Mummy can't jet ice out of her hands. As far as I know. She says her milk cravings have calmed down, which is good, although now she just wants to eat junk. She said they gave her this healthy lunch of salmon and pearl barley and sautéed vegetables today and she had to rush back to the car to speed-eat a packet of Twinkies.

Daddy went to Washington to visit my pal President Obama. They FaceTimed me from a place called the Oval Office and did animal impressions to make me laugh. President Obama can make a noise EXACTLY like a dolphin.

10th December

Daddy was literally hysterical on today's call. That's because he and Mummy went to a basketball match last night and met some people called Jay Z and Beyoncé. They are musicians and they are almost as famous as we are.

'Seriously, Georgie, these people are like ROYALTY,' Daddy said. 'And yet they still manage to be, you know, really chill.'

Mummy started sniggering. 'Prince Will.i.am just entered the building,' she said.

'I thought Beyoncé was dope, didn't you?' Daddy said.

'Whoa,' Mummy said. 'Is this actually happening?'

'Fresh,' Daddy said.

'OK,' Mummy said. 'Let me translate, George. What Daddy is trying to say is that he was excited to meet Jay

Z and Beyoncé and that they are very nice people.' She then held up a basketball top. 'Also this is a present for you from the Cleveland Cavaliers. A man called Le-Bron James with feet the size of Windsor Castle gave it to you on behalf of the team.'

'Good one, Shorty,' Daddy said.

'Can we get a hip-hop adviser in for my husband, please,' Mummy said to their Travel Secretary, 'before he says any of this in public and we're thrown out of the country?'

11th December

Mummy and Daddy are home again.

Daddy has not stopped obsessively checking his phone.

'Not going to happen,' Mummy said to him this afternoon.

'It might,' Daddy said.

'It won't.'

'But I felt a real connection.'

'No, you didn't.'

'Like we could really be friends.'

'Look at me,' Mummy said, putting down her bottle of peacock-oil hair treatment. 'Jay Z is not going to text you.'

'He asked for my number, though.'

'No, you gave it to him.'

Daddy's phone beeped and he jumped with excitement. 'Please let it be him!' Then his face fell. 'It's from Spike.'

'What does it say?' Mummy asked.

'He's asking me how many problems I've got, and if he were to hazard a guess, would it come in at ninety-nine?'

'Well,' Mummy said, raising an eyebrow, 'I'm assuming I'm not one of them.'

14th December

They released those photos for my Christmas Cheer campaign today and all seems to have gone well. And when I say well, I mean brilliantly. And when I say brilliantly, I mean the entire planet has gone into meltdown.

My team is very pleased with the result.

'It's official,' my Press Secretary said, in our meeting today. 'Christmas Cheer is now the nation's official mood.'

Everyone clapped.

'We're experiencing a tremendous response online for copycat looks,' my stylist said. 'I never get tired of saying that.'

'And we never get tired of hearing it,' my Press Secretary said. 'Excellent work, Sir. Excellent work, team.'

Everyone clapped again.

'The reaction is just . . .' my head of Global Strategy said '. . . well, it's through the roof. It's off the chart. It's headline news. Globally.'

More clapping.

'I'd call that a Merry Christmas!' my Movement Interpreter cheered.

'Hooray!' everyone shouted.

A good day at the office.

15th December

The Present Team has started a relay system to cope with the increased levels of Christmas deliveries from around the world. There is always someone on standby at the door, so that when it rings, the present can be rushed to the Present Room and logged. It's so organized.

By the way, I'm still not sure what all the fuss is about this Father Christmas fellow. Apparently you write him a letter asking him for things you want and if you've been good he brings them to you. How does it work when that already happens but without you having to write a letter first? Or be good? He didn't really think this through, did he?

16th December

Mummy said she went to see some beavers today. The beavers blindfolded her and then made her ice cup-cakes and then they put her in boxing gloves and made her eat chocolate with a plastic fork. She said the whole thing was completely excellent and maybe one day I'd like to be a beaver. I had no idea what on earth she was talking about. I already know from my Zoologist that beavers build dams with their teeth and I haven't even got all my molars through yet.

17th December

The mystery is solved. Beavers are Boy Scouts, not just semi-aquatic rodents. I know this because of the pictures of Mummy in the newspaper today. My fears that I will be expected to live in a wet house, made of branches and mud that I built with my own mouth, and eat pondweed have subsequently been alleviated.

We went to HQ today. David seemed a bit anxious in his meeting with GG.

'Be honest, Ma'am,' he said as soon as he arrived, 'do you think I've put on weight?'

'I really couldn't say, Prime Minister,' GG said. 'Perhaps I see you too often to notice any change?'

'That's exactly what Sam said, which means you think I have.' David looked worried. 'Otherwise you'd just say no.'

'I'm sure she doesn't think that,' GG said. 'You look fine to me.'

'Fine, but not "thin",' David said.

'Do you want to look thin?' GG asked diplomatically.

'I can afford to lose a couple of pounds, perhaps,' David said. 'Maybe.'

The tea tray was brought in. The sandwiches glistened.

'And yet I'm just so hungry,' David said, staring at the tray. 'And it's not like I don't exercise. The stress of Prime Minister's Questions definitely helps me burn calories.'

'I'm sure it does,' GG said.

'And fighting with Nick is like a session at the gym sometimes,' David said. 'Not physically fighting, obviously. Apart from that one time, but that was because of a misunderstanding.'

'Oh dear,' GG said.

'I never said he had big hands,' David said. 'Or a gigantic face.'

GG raised her eyebrows.

'The thing is, though,' David said quietly, 'he sort of does. But it wasn't me who said it. That's the point.'

'Horrid to be misquoted,' GG said.

'He won't stop going on about it. It's very draining. I

use up a lot of nervous energy constantly trying to defend myself.'

'Well,' GG said, 'let us serve ourselves by remembering that Christmas is a time of peace and goodwill to all men.'

'Exactly. I'll start by serving myself a piece of that gingerbread,' David said, taking two pieces. 'I don't know what I'd do without your advice, Ma'am.'

18th December

Mummy and Daddy are really excited about Father Christmas, which is making no sense to me.

'What are you going to ask him for?' Mummy asked Daddy today.

'Safety for all animals,' Daddy said. 'What are you going to ask him for?'

'I want a large box of Krispy Kremes,' Mummy said seriously. 'The classic glazed ones that I could microwave so that the glaze melts a bit and the dough becomes even softer.'

'Imagine . . .' Daddy said.

'I know, yum,' Mummy said.

'No, imagine knowing how to use a microwave.'

Mummy's dietary requirements continue to get worse. All she wants to eat is sugary things and fast food but the kitchen only makes her healthy dishes. She asked for a hotdog the other day but it was all organic and homemade from a pig that lived on apple pressé and truffles. She was so disappointed.

Daddy says she got so obsessed with Twinkies when they were in New York that she wouldn't leave the hotel room unless she had filled her handbag and everyone's pockets with them. This has now changed to Jaffa Cakes. Boxes of them have replaced the cartons of milk in every room.

'Are they a cake or a biscuit?' Daddy asked her today.

'Who cares?' Mummy said, roaring through a packet at double speed.

19th December

The Present Team have now formed a human chain from the front door to the Present Room. It's easier for them to just pass the presents down in a long line as the doorbell is ringing so incessantly that there isn't time to leave their posts. And the Logging Team has been doubled. Maybe Father Christmas would like some of this stuff for redistribution. Wonder if anyone will have had the forethought to look into that and got hold of his email?

We are going to Anmer for Christmas tomorrow, so

my Wardrobe Team has been meeting all day. My Christmas outfit options are currently looking like this:

Elf
Christmas pudding
Christmas tree
Candy cane
Robin
Father Christmas
Reindeer
Snowman
Snowball

They have been discussing strategies as I expect to change at least three times a day over this period to make sure I incorporate every look. And people think Mummy has it tough.

20th December

We are at Anmer, yay. I was so excited about being here I decided to shout about it at 2 a.m. Then at 3.30 a.m., then at 5 a.m. – when, quite frankly, it was time to get up because there is so much to do. Mummy and Daddy didn't seem to be that happy about my enthusiasm. They both looked like Uncle Harry did that time he'd been out with his army friends and ended up sleeping in a bin.

21st December

Today we went to the Anmer church service to say happy birthday to Jesus and to sing some songs about someone called Gloria. Jesus is going to be 2,014 years old in four days' time. I wonder if G-Pop knows him?

I thoroughly enjoyed myself actually and shouted to show it. Mummy and Daddy kept trying to tell me to be quiet, but I knew all eyes were on me. I wanted to give people a show because otherwise it would all just have been sitting still for ages without talking and who wants to do that? So I threw some hymnbooks around, repeatedly kicked the back of our pew, blurted out streams of enthusiastic consciousness during the homily and didn't sit still for longer than about twelve seconds at a time. It was a hoot – although when we got home, Mummy said there was no way I was allowed to come to church on Christmas Day because I was too loud, and Daddy agreed. Uncle Harry is disappointed.

'The vicar would literally have to shout to be heard,' Daddy said. 'It's not really fair on everyone.'

'I'm tempted to start randomly shouting through the service myself. Then maybe I'll be allowed to stay at home too,' Uncle Harry said.

'But what if you weren't there and someone in the crowd inevitably gave me a present to give you?' Daddy said.

'Let's say, for the sake of argument, a Cadbury's Christmas Stocking,' Mummy said, staring into the middle distance.

'You try being the person who tells Kate she can't rip it open in front of everyone and have the Crunchie because it's specifically meant to be for you,' Daddy said.

'Don't joke about that, please,' Mummy said.

'You're right, of course,' Uncle Harry said. 'I can't run the risk of Two Ton Tessie here gorging herself like a hyena on the general public's kind donations to my present drawer.'

'I'm glad we understand each other,' Mummy said. 'Now, go and get me some smoky bacon crisps before this inexplicable hunger confuses me and I take a bite out of your leg.'

Uncle Harry says he is going to start wearing shin pads until Ringo is born.

24th December

Today is a day called Christmas Eve! Aunt P, Uncle J, Granny C and Grandpa M have arrived. Grandpa M is dressed as a cracker.

We spent most of the day at Sandringham because, don't spread it around, but we are a bit German and our German ancestors always opened their presents on Christmas Eve, so we do too. Uncle Harry says being a bit German doesn't count, particularly when it's the World Cup – unless Germany beat England and then go on to win the whole thing, in which case it absolutely does count.

First we had tea and then we got stuck in. The rule is you only get a joke present because we get so much stuff all year round. GG was very pleased with her 'Drama Queen' eye mask and wore it on her forehead for the rest of the evening, and G-Pop was so thrilled with his packet of Tesco Finest Pork Sausages that he switched on the electric frying-pan he's so devoted to immediately and cooked the lot in the drawing room.

I got a good haul, even though it's really against protocol for me to get presents at Christmas. I enjoyed the tearing-paper bit the most and tried to offer my paper-ripping services to other members of the family. Well, when I say 'offer' I mean I just launched in and tore indiscriminately at any present I found.

Mummy's present was a sick bag that had been filled with pick 'n' mix and Daddy's present was a packet of false moustaches, which were quickly distributed between everyone. GG said she wanted the big blond droopy one called the 'Hulk Hogan', Uncle Harry wore the 'Dalí', Mummy wore the 'Einstein' and Daddy wore the 'Chaplin'. Great Aunt Annie ended up with the 'Magnum PI', but she didn't seem to find it as funny as everyone else.

'Look, this is all very amusing,' she said, pursing her

now incredibly busy top lip, 'but what's happening with the games?'

'We'll do all that tomorrow,' GG said, looking a bit nervous.

'I just want a heads-up on what's been planned,' Great Aunt Annie said seriously. 'So I can start strategizing.' Then she asked if anyone wanted a quick game of Racing Demon. It totally changed the mood in the room. GaGa said she couldn't because her back was hurting too much and Goonie said he couldn't because he hadn't finished his conversation with the mistletoe. Great Uncle Andy and Great Uncle Eddie said they couldn't because they wanted to watch *Elf* on TV, Great Aunt Soph hid under the table and Cousin Bea and Cousin Euge just ran out of the room.

As Great Aunt Annie made a beeline for GG and G-Pop to see if she could commandeer them, Daddy turned to us. 'We only have seconds left,' he said breathily. 'She'll be over at any moment – what do we do?'

'Quick, George,' Mummy said. 'Go and knock over that vase.'

'But it was a present from Franklin Roosevelt to Great Grandpa Bertie,' Daddy said anxiously.

'This is an emergency!' Mummy whispered. 'I'm thinking of all of us!'

Great Aunt Annie, who didn't seem to be getting anywhere with GG and G-Pop, both of whom had suddenly pretended to fall asleep, finally turned her determined gaze upon us. I rushed at the vase, giving it a hearty wallop and watched it crash to the floor. The only problem was, it didn't break. Mummy and Daddy looked at each other with panic-riddled saucer-eyes, so Daddy subtly stepped onto its neck and we heard it crack under his foot. Great Aunt Annie eyed us all suspiciously. 'Well, you kids, who's got the *cojones* to take me on at a round of RD?' she said menacingly.

'George just broke this vase.' Daddy gulped. 'A present from Rooselin Frankevelt – I mean, Franklin Roosevelt. Better get someone to, you know, maybe see if it can be fixed.' He backed away towards the curtains.

'Kate. I know you love a spirited game of festive cards,' Great Aunt Annie said.

Mummy frowned. 'Feeling so sick,' she whispered, pointing at her bump. 'Sorry.'

There was only one man left. Uncle Harry sat paralysed in his chair, a terrible tortured smile on his face.

'YOU,' Great Aunt Annie boomed.

'Hay, Aunt A,' Uncle Harry squeaked. The faintest hint of a smile appeared on Mummy's face.

'How about a quick friendly game?'

Uncle Harry looked at us frantically. 'Aaah . . . aaaah . . . aaaaah,' was all he could say.

'What's it to be? Yay or nay?'

Uncle Harry shot a glance to Mummy. 'Neigh?' he said.

But she made him play anyway. He's got a bandage on his hand now. Apparently Great Aunt Annie got so violent in her bid to secure the pile of spades with her king that she slammed her fist down instead of the card and Uncle Harry's hand got in the way.

'It was an accident,' Great Aunt Annie said. 'But he didn't move fast enough and that's not my fault. The main thing is, I won.'

It's a bit swollen and bruised, but Uncle Harry says he's just grateful to still have the use of his fingers.

Anyway, we hung our stockings up by the fireplace before we went to bed and left out a treat for Father Christmas because that is the tradition. It was a Duchy Originals mince pie and a glass of something called Pol Roger.

'He must be sick of those things,' Uncle Harry said, prodding the mince pie. 'I bet he'd rather have a burger.'

'Or a pork pie,' Mummy said wistfully.

She got out a pencil, opened her letter to Father Christmas and added 'pork pie' to the bottom of her wish list.

25th December

Today is a day called Christmas Day! Jesus must be so excited!

Christmas is a bit like everyone having their birthday at the same time – THAT is how much fun it is. My choir woke me up with a rousing rendition of 'I Saw Three Ships' and Mummy, Daddy and Uncle Harry came jumping into my room to take me downstairs to see if Father Christmas had visited in the night.

Our stockings were bulging by the fireplace.

'He's been!!!' Uncle Harry shouted.

The drink was gone! The mince pie was gone! Lupo had been sick on the floor in a mince pie shape, but that was just a coincidence!

We all got into Mummy and Daddy's bed to open our stockings. It's so big there was room for Granny C, Grandpa M, Aunt P and Uncle J too. Everyone was allowed to ask Mummy and Daddy's choir for their favourite Christmas song – and then we all sang along! Except me! Because I can't really talk yet! I just shouted generally – particularly during Uncle Harry's choice, which was a really stupid song called 'Christmas Is All Around'.

Then they all got changed out of their Christmas pyjamas and went to church and when they got back, everyone was laughing because apparently a speaker played them singing to the crowd outside and Uncle Harry said it was 'horrendous'. G-Pop was singing a completely different hymn, Great Aunt Annie was in the wrong key and Uncle Harry's harmonizing with

Daddy didn't work at all. Mummy said it was like listening to a group of ill cats having a fight on a fence.

After that we went to the big house for lunch, but when we arrived, a complicated thing happened in the hall. It's all because GG updated the Order of Precedence to accommodate Daddy marrying Mummy. She has a terrible time trying to keep everyone happy in the family and sometimes that means changing the rules to keep the peace. People get married, people have babies – the order of everything shifts around constantly. It's a minefield. These changes were meant to help, but they haven't really.

There we were in the hall when Daddy said he had to ring Godfather Jamie, so he stepped into the doorway of another room. Just then Cousin Bea and Cousin Euge came downstairs. If Daddy isn't with her, Mummy has to curtsy to them because they are princesses by blood. If he is, they're supposed to curtsy to her. Those are the rules.

'Happy Christmas!' they shouted. 'Hashtag jingle bell vibes!'

'Happy Christmas!' Mummy replied.

They all looked at Daddy, who loitered in the doorway.

'Is he in the room or not?' Mummy said. 'He's got one foot on either side of the doorway. What do we do?'

'Like, I have no idea,' Cousin Euge said.

'Is it us or you?' Cousin Bea said cheerfully.

'I'd rather be on the safe side,' Mummy said politely, starting to curtsy. Just as Daddy temporarily stepped back into the hall. With both feet.

'Wait, he's back in the room!' Cousin Euge and Cousin Bea shrieked.

Mummy quickly stood up again and Cousin Euge and Cousin Bea curtsied instead. It was like they were on a seesaw.

Then Great Uncle Eddie and Great Aunt Soph came sloping down the stairs too.

'Hullo,' they said. 'Happy Christmas.'

Everyone looked at Daddy.

'We can't tell if Wills is, like, in the room or not in the room,' Cousin Euge said.

'Awky mo-mo,' Cousin Bea said.

'That doesn't affect me,' Great Aunt Soph said tightly, curtsying to absolutely everyone.

'Oh Lord,' Uncle Harry whispered to me. 'This is a better start to the day than I could ever have imagined.'

Then GaGa and Goonie came down the stairs.

'Ahoy!' GaGa said. 'Happy Christmas, lovers!'

Everyone curtsied to them. At least that was straightforward.

Then Great Aunt Annie came down the stairs.

'Happy Christmas,' she boomed. 'Who wants a quick-fire game of Snakes and Ladders before lunch?'

Everyone looked at Daddy. Who had stepped back and now had feet on either side of the doorway again.

'Isn't this a scream?' GaGa said cheerfully. 'Shall I send Fred away and really shake things up?' She and Goonie laughed hysterically.

'Actually, I do need to ask William something,' Goonie said, heading off towards Daddy.

Great Aunt Annie looked at GaGa. 'So, this is awkward,' she said flatly.

'Down I go!' GaGa said, bending her knees to curtsy.

Uncle Harry was by this time so hysterical that he had to go and stand by one of the Titians until he had calmed down.

'Thanks for that, Wombat,' he said later on, getting a ten-pound note out of his pocket and giving it to Daddy as we were going up the stairs. 'It worked like a dream. I haven't laughed that much in ages.'

'What the hell?' Mummy said. 'You planned that?'

Daddy looked guilty.

'We just wanted to test if everyone knew the rules,' Uncle Harry said. 'Pa leaving the room too was an unexpected bonus.'

Mummy gave him a shove.

'You are so dead,' she said. 'I'll get you for this. From now on, you need to sleep with one eye open.'

Daddy laughed, so Mummy shoved him too.

'As for you,' she said, menacingly, 'you're sleeping on the sofa for the rest of your life.'

'I love you,' he called after her, as she marched past him, deliberately treading on his foot.

Anyway, we had a jolly lunch with everyone sitting round the big table and me in a high chair that used to belong to another George (the fifth one). Uncle Harry had to change the place names round so that Mummy was sitting opposite Great Aunt Annie because of that bet she lost.

By the time it came to pulling the crackers, I'd got a bit fed up of being in my chair so had been let out and was running around to see what everyone was up to. G-Pop stopped me in my tracks and asked that I be put on his lap.

'I already have one foot in Abraham's bosom,' G-Pop said to me, 'and Annie rushing at me with a cracker might prove to be curtains. I'm going to be frank – it's possible I'll have to use you to physically deflect her.'

Great Aunt Annie suddenly reared up over us, thrusting a large cracker at G-Pop. 'PULL IT,' she instructed.

I held onto it too to try to help G-Pop.

'PULL HARDER,' Great Aunt Annie barked.

'I'll give you this baby if you leave me alone,' G-Pop said.

Great Aunt Annie yanked violently on the cracker and it snapped in her hand. 'I WIN,' she shouted triumphantly. She looked around the table. 'Who wants to pull another cracker?' Everyone looked into their laps or pretended they hadn't heard.

I went off for another wander and stopped by GG. She tapped her knee, so I clambered up onto her lap.

'Have you seen the Prince of Wales?' GG asked the butler.

'He's reciting Coleridge's "This Lime-tree Bower My Prison" to the Christmas tree, Ma'am,' he replied.

GG sighed. 'I don't know what you think, George, but can one really be expected to believe that cropped plants respond to conversation? They're not growing. What is, in fact, the benefit?' She shook her head. 'He gets so batey when I bring it up. "Do let me do things my way, Mummy" and "Darling, magical Granny always understood" and "By the way, I still have nightmares about getting whacked on the head for snoring at Gordonstoun". I suppose one oughtn't to be bothered by it, with so many more serious things in the world, but he's going to be in the Top Job one day and sometimes I think it makes him look like he hasn't got both oars in the water, if you know what I mean.'

'When do we start the games?' Great Aunt Annie asked for the tenth time.

'Ask your father,' GG said.

'He told me to ask you,' Great Aunt Annie said.

GG looked over at G-Pop. 'Judas,' she muttered very quietly.

'What's that?' Great Aunt Annie asked.

'I said "I can't wait",' GG said.

'Good,' Great Aunt Annie said, starting to do some stretches.

GG and I watched her.

'I am Commander-in-Chief of the Armed Forces,' GG said to herself. 'I can do this.'

The games part started off well. Everyone got into two lines and had a race to see which team could pass a balloon under their chins the fastest – but then Cousin Bea got into a panic and accidentally burst her team's balloon with her teeth.

Great Aunt Annie went wild shouting, 'WE WIN! WE WIN!' and then someone got the Pictionary out. When it was G-Pop's turn to draw, everyone got so confused that half his team gave up.

'Is it a loaf of bread?' GG said, trying to be sporting.

'Bread?' G-Pop shouted, in disbelief.

'What are those dots?' GG asked. 'Raisins? Is it raisin bread?'

'Those are eyes! It's obviously a platypus!' G-Pop said, flinging his pencil down. 'You're blind, you're all bloody blind.'

'So it is,' GG said calmly. 'And now I can see that the likeness is remarkable. It's marvellous, really.'

GG has a line for every occasion.

Then Great Uncle Eddie said, 'Showtime, Mummy,' and he switched on GG giving her speech on TV.

'Oh no, not this,' GG said. 'What time is *Downton*

on?' She gave me her handbag to play with and I went through it as usual. There was that stone again. I rolled it around a bit and ate some of the Mean Girls' dog chocs. GG picked up the stone and rubbed it gently between her finger and thumb – but she didn't want a dog choc when I tried to feed her one.

Then we played charades. When it was Aunt P's turn, she stood in front of everyone and mimed 'film'. Then she held up two fingers. For the first word, she made a "T" with her hands.

'The!' everyone said.

She tugged on her ear.

'Sounds like!' everyone said.

Then she pointed to the top of her ribcage.

'Heart?' Uncle Harry said.

'Chest?' Mummy shouted.

'Shirt?' Grandpa M shouted.

Aunt P shook her head.

'Ridiculous girl?' G-Pop shouted.

'Finger?' Cousin Euge shouted.

Aunt P shook her head.

'You might be too clever for us,' GaGa said. 'We give up.'

'No, we don't!' Great Aunt Annie snapped.

'What else might it rhyme with, do you suppose?' Goonic said.

Aunt P shrugged. 'I can't think of anything,' she said.

'No talking!' Great Aunt Annie said. 'Why am I the only one who cares about the rules?'

'I know what it is,' Uncle Harry said. 'It's spleen. As in Queen. The answer is *The Queen*.'

There was silence.

'Perhaps it might have been an idea to just point at me?' GG said politely.

'Oh yes,' Aunt P said cheerfully. 'I didn't think of that.'

Everyone seemed a bit surprised.

'The good news is,' Uncle Harry said, 'that I thought no one could be more terrible at charades than me – but now I've found someone even worse. You know what this means, P?'

Aunt P shook her head.

'We are meant to be together,' Uncle Harry said. 'You know I'm right.'

'Errr . . .' Aunt P said, doubtfully.

'And that's not all,' Uncle Harry said. 'That "no ring" nonsense you were grumbling about before? Well, this time, I've come prepared.' He shook half of his cracker and a large neon-yellow plastic ring fell out. 'If it doesn't fit, we can get it resized.' He went over to Aunt P and put it on the ring finger of her left hand.

Aunt P held her hand out. 'Hmmm,' she said, regarding the ring. 'I just don't think it's really me.'

'Listen, cutie,' Uncle Harry said. 'I had to fight Aunt Annie for that – don't be ungrateful.'

Aunt P took the ring off and handed it back to Uncle Harry. 'I'm afraid it's a "no" from me,' she said. 'But thanks. And Happy Christmas.'

'I don't believe this,' Uncle Harry said. 'That's twice she's turned me down. I'm going to develop a complex if this carries on.'

'That's still not an excuse to cheat at charades,' Daddy said. 'I saw you with your phone under the table.'

'Wait. You Googled the answer?' Great Aunt Annie said to Uncle Harry.

'Might have done,' Uncle Harry said.

'Just so we're all clear, that does not count,' Great Aunt Annie told the room. 'Harry cheated. That is NOT a point to your team.'

'Yes, that was a "whoooaaa-ful" abandonment of the rules,' Mummy said, shooting a glance at Uncle Harry. 'You've been misbehaving ever since we sat down at this stable.'

'What?' Great Aunt Annie said.

'This table,' Mummy repeated.

Uncle Harry let out a terrible squawk and that made Daddy completely hysterical.

'What's the matter with those two?' Great Aunt Annie said.

'I have no idea,' Mummy said. 'They always stirrup trouble whenever they're together.'

It's the end of an excellent day. What I have learnt is that Christmas is not just about the presents. It's also about family. Because without your family, you would have to play pass the balloon on your own and that would be impossible. Also, pulling crackers would be less fun.

I'm so happy. I hope it's Christmas again tomorrow.

26th December

It is not Christmas again today. It is a day called Boxing Day. That is because there are so many boxes to clear up after Christmas because of all the presents and food and decorations. Uncle Harry stayed up really late last night playing cards with Uncle J and gambling with chocolate from the general public while drinking Horse's Necks. Today he looks like a ghost. Mummy is so pleased with him, though. She lay on the sofa for most of the afternoon making her way through his winnings while everyone else went off for the Boxing Day shoot. And Grandpa M decided not to wear his pheasant fancy dress after Granny C pointed out it would be so awkward if G-Pop shot him by accident.

29th December

We are spending the time mostly playing games and going for walks. Sometimes Ringo kicks Mummy and we can see her actual stomach moving. It's sort of interesting and gross at the same time.

Uncle Harry always shouts, 'ALIEN!' when that happens and then makes a kind of exploding noise, but I don't really know what that means.

31st December

Today is the last day of the year. Next year Ringo will be here and everything will be different. Everyone had to say what they were most looking forward to in 2015 and every single one of them said Ringo being born. Mummy looked very happy and rubbed the bump, saying, 'Did you hear that, Ringo? We can't wait until you're here.'

Ringo obviously kicked when she said that and everyone thought it was marvellous. I kick things day in day out and am therefore in a position to say with authority that being able to kick is an unremarkable talent. Ringo is going to have to rely on other skills in the future if it wants to get by.

Uncle J was busy all afternoon making New Year cupcakes and Aunt P decorated the house for the New Year's Eve party, but it made no difference to me because I was still in bed by seven thirty.

Daddy gave me my milk and we read a story and at the end he said, 'See you next year!'

This year has been very good, all in all, and I've been reflecting on my achievements. Learnt to walk, brought down the internet a few times, saved the odd species of animal. And then there was developing a strong urge not to share anything, working out how to eat on my own and learning how to say things like 'cat', 'no' and 'commonwealth'.

Not bad for seventeen months on the planet.

January 2015

1st January 2015

It's 2015! Happy New Year!

Last night they all stayed up again playing games and fooling around. Uncle Harry was still asleep in the gunroom when I had breakfast this morning, wearing a pair of antlers with bells on them and with one of Daddy's fake moustaches stuck to his cheek. Daddy has 'I AM A WOMBAT' written in ink that won't come off across his forehead and Uncle J has half his beard missing because they shaved it off for LOLZ when he fell asleep on the sofa.

Anyway, they were all quite grumpy today. Granny C insisted everyone be washed and dressed for lunch, but they were extremely untalkative, even when Grandpa M asked what everyone's New Year Resolutions were.

A New Year Resolution is something you decide you are going to do. Like 'I am going to walk this year' or 'I am going to grow some new teeth' or 'I am going to learn to say a few words' (those were last year's Resolutions).

I need to think of some new ones. I might start with 'forming full sentences', 'sharing my toys with other children without fighting', 'putting on my own trousers', 'learning to wave at people from cars', and go from there.

3rd January

It's a bit boring around here at the moment. Everyone keeps falling asleep in the afternoons. I therefore decided to make a list of the top twenty things I like the most in the world. New Year is a time for reflection, after all. This is what I thought of:

1. Crocodiles
2. Painting pictures of crocodiles
3. Football
4. GG's stone
5. Slamming doors
6. When Uncle Harry sits on Daddy's head
7. Splashing in the bath
8. GG's impression of someone called Helen Mirren
9. Mummy's hair
10. Mummy

11. Feeding Lupo my spinach when no one is looking
12. Uncle J's cupcakes
13. When GaGa chases Goonie with her bee smoker
14. Christmas
15. Birthdays
16. Playing games when you're on Great Aunt Annie's team
17. Australia
18. Uncle Harry's dancing
19. The general public
20. G-Pop

I may swap feeding Lupo out for sandpits or eating grass, but I haven't decided yet. The point is, I have realized that I have another twenty things I love just queuing up and that is a good sign about life. I love this country. If I'm going to be king of anywhere, I'm glad it's here. Although the moon would also be fun.

8th January

We are so excited because it's Mummy's birthday tomorrow!!!! Daddy has been scheming with Uncle Harry, Aunt P and Uncle J all day to arrange lovely things for her. She said she doesn't want a fuss, but when Daddy said, 'Really?' she replied, 'Of course not really.'

9th January

HAPPY BIRTHDAY, MUMMY!!!!!!! She is thirty-three years old. What must it be like to be so incredibly ancient??? Everyone came downstairs in their pyjamas to find a party hat that said 'Weighty Katie' on their plate at breakfast this morning and Mummy was given a big cake decorated with sweets that Uncle J had made. She was so happy.

'Yum!' Daddy said, after we'd sung 'Happy Birthday' to her. 'I'll gather up the plates while you cut the cake.'

'Er, I don't think so,' Mummy said, putting her arm protectively around it. 'This is MY cake.' And she just dug her hand into it and put it in her mouth.

'Look at her go!' Uncle Harry said. 'She's like a deranged Viking.'

Mummy flung a chunk of cake at Uncle Harry when he said that, a wild glint in her eye.

'Foolish,' Uncle Harry said, smiling and wiping it off his face. 'Very, very foolish.' He lunged at Mummy, grabbing a large handful of the cake and rubbing it all over her face.

'Here we go,' Daddy said. 'Take cover, Georgie.'

Mummy scooped up a huge handful and chased after Daddy, who ran around the dining-room table roaring with laughter. Uncle J shoved a big piece of the cake down the back of Aunt P's pyjamas and Aunt P rubbed a big piece into Uncle Harry's hair. Everyone was screaming.

Mummy cornered Daddy, who tried to fend her off by pushing against her forehead and holding her at arm's length, but she drove her finger into his armpit, and when his guard was down, she splattered a whole piece in his face and rammed a second piece up his pyjama top.

It was chaos. AND SO BRILLIANT!

Ten minutes later, everyone was sitting on the floor eating bits of birthday cake while Mummy opened some of her presents. Uncle Harry licked the palm of his hand and said, 'This is really delicious, by the way, J.'

Uncle J was so pleased and explained the recipe in detail. He said he is actually planning a cake replica of his girlfriend for her birthday later in the year. To scale. He's so clever.

'Here,' Daddy said to me. 'You must try some too, G. It is a special occasion after all.' And he fed me a bit on his finger. I wish we could have chocolate cake covered in sweets for breakfast every day. I think I'm going to start a 'Notes for the Top Job' book to keep abreast of the changes I intend to make.

Mummy's favourite present was a packet of something called Cheese Strings and some Cadbury's mini rolls. The only way Daddy could get her to see the other present he bought her was by dropping a trail of sweets on the floor all the way to the wall where it hung.

It's a painting. By someone called Rembrandt.

11th January

We're back in London. Ringo's room is being decorated and Mummy has been opening the deliveries of clothes she's been ordering for it. They are the smallest things I've ever seen. I tried to put on one of the hats but it was too tiny. Good for carrying cars and pens around, though.

12th January

I listened to Mummy's tummy today to see if I could hear Ringo saying anything, but I couldn't. Mummy explained that Ringo is living in a sack of liquid at the moment, like a fish. What she is basically saying is that Ringo can swim underwater. I cannot believe that Ringo is already better at swimming than me.

14th January

Went swimming with Mummy at HQ today. Thought about Ringo floating around in Mummy's internal tank. Got quite cross with my armbands so tried to pull them off and ended up swallowing half the pool. Then I went to play with David and GG.

'Before we start,' David said, 'I need to make an announcement.'

'Go on,' GG said, listening attentively.

'I'm going on a diet,' David said.

'Right,' GG said.

'Now, I know what you're probably thinking,' David said. 'What does he need to go on a diet for?'

'Well . . .' GG said.

'But Christmas is so unforgiving when it comes to food,' he said, pinching his waistline. 'I mean, I don't even like cake that much – but it's hard to say no when someone offers it to you because that's just bad manners.'

GG raised her eyebrows.

'So I'm giving up bread,' David said resolutely. 'It's going to be my great patriotic struggle. I will not be eating any bread from this day on. Or biscuits or cake. I am a wheat-free man.'

They both looked at the tea tray with the plate of sandwiches and the fruitcake.

'Shall I ask to have it removed?' GG said.

'No, no,' David said. 'I'm strong. I am strong.'

'Very good,' GG said.

'And it's about time I was reminded what some serious opposition felt like!'

He laughed loudly. And then he looked a bit serious.

'It can't hurt to look can it?' he said, staring sorrowfully at the biscuits. 'I've started running as well. That's meant to be good for you, isn't it?'

'I believe it is,' GG said. 'Perhaps we might turn our attention to interest rates, Prime Minister?'

'Are those bourbons?' David asked, moving slowly towards the tray.

In other news, Uncle Harry was given a size-fifteen shoe by a basketball player called Carmelo Anthony at the Coach Core graduation ceremony at St James's Palace today.

'You could move into it,' Daddy said, 'and have room for guests.'

'I wonder if we could actually fit Small G into it, like a sort of canoe?' Uncle Harry said to Daddy.

It wasn't comfortable, but I was able to squeeze into it. Then Uncle Harry pushed me around a bit like it was a boat and Daddy pretended to be a mutant octopus chasing us. That bit was totally brilliant.

15th January

When I saw Mummy this evening, she was lying on the sofa eating something called a Viennetta, which she'd got one of her security detail to sneak in for her, after what she says was a totally ace day. Apparently she opened an art room for a school with a girl called Claire, who sometimes calls herself Grayson Perry.

17th January

Mummy came back from work today with a present for me: an inflatable duck-shaped rubber ring. I played with it in the bath tonight and, as the world's most prolific splasher, decided to see if I could splash enough water out to make it float on the floor. It worked! Even my Bath Team were impressed! At least, I think they were. It was quite hard to tell with their diving masks.

20th January

We are going on holiday in a couple of days and I'm so excited about flying on a plane. We are travelling to a place called Mustique, which is where Great Great

Aunt Margaret liked to wear a turban and smoke her Chesterfields with someone called Mick Jagger.

23rd January

Here. Mustique. Hot. Jetlagged.

24th January

What time is it? Why is it dark outside? So awake. Mummy keeps saying, 'Go back to sleep,' but I want to go and spot dolphins.

25th January

Haven't seen any dolphins yet. Or pirate ships. It's HOT.

27th January

Feeling more normal now. Today we played on the beach and Grandpa M and I built some sandcastles together. We made HQ and then we made Windsor Castle with my special HQ and Windsor Castle buckets and then we put some seaweed on the top for flags and some shells around the outside for guards. And then it got so hot that Grandpa M had to take his crab costume off.

28th January

Mummy says if Daddy doesn't wear more sun cream, he will end up on someone's plate when he is inevitably mistaken for a lobster.

'Are you changing your name to Thermidor?' Mummy asked Daddy.

'Just trying to get a bit of colour,' Daddy replied.

'What is it with you people?' Mummy said, looking at Daddy, Grandpa M and Uncle J. 'Why don't men understand that sun cream doesn't stop you tanning, it stops you burning?'

'All right,' Daddy said, with his bright red chest. 'But I only need factor eight.'

'I'm fine with factor four,' Grandpa M said, with his bright red nose.

'And I'm fine with this coconut tanning oil,' Uncle J said, with his bright red shoulders.

'I'll have you with garlic butter, you with hollandaise and you with a side order of fries,' Mummy said, pointing at each of them. 'Please wait in the swimming pool and I will personally select who is first for the pot.'

29th January

A day lazing around the pool. Not me, obviously. I spent the whole day IN the pool splashing and shouting and swimming with Daddy. I'm sorry my crocodile isn't here because I feel like he would really be enjoying himself.

31st January

Today is Granny C's birthday! She is SIXTY!!!!!!!! Mummy says that's two Uncle Harrys put together!

Uncle J spent the day baking, of course, while Aunt P decorated the house for our party. Grandpa M was so excited, he dressed up as a birthday cake, even though it made him sweat so much he kept having to fan himself with the plastic knife that went with it.

We had a little party in the evening, where everyone had to tell their favourite story about Granny C and she laughed and then she cried, but it was fine because it was happy crying and that is the best kind, Mummy says. Uncle J made her a cake shaped like a wheelie-suitcase and Grandpa M sang her a song called 'Come Fly With Me' and then she cried again. At the end she gave us all party bags that she'd made herself to say thank you. I had some finger snakes, a superhero mask and a fire engine in mine. Mummy had a water pistol in hers, so everyone went to bed completely drenched.

February 2015

3rd February

Today we went on a boat. We still haven't seen any pirates, but it was OK because we saw someone called Johnny Depp instead and Mummy said that was sort of the same thing.

5th February

Sand really does get everywhere, doesn't it?

7th February

I know I have a responsibility to the fashion industry, but part of me wishes I didn't have to wear clothes again. Roaming around for two weeks with no kit on has been very freeing. (Wait – how DID that bit of sand get THERE?)

9th February

We're leaving Mustique today and I'm sad. I think I may spend the fourteen-hour plane journey home trying to communicate that.

10th February

Jetlag. Confused. Is it the day or the middle of the night? What and where and who and what?

11th February

Mummy and Daddy were so excited that I woke up late this morning. They were less excited about me waking up three times in the night, though. Whoever invented jetlag should be put in the Tower, I'm afraid.

Did some painting with Mummy today – she painted lots of boats while I painted a picture of my pirate, Johnny. I felt like it had come out terribly well until Mummy said, 'That's good, Georgie – is it a snake?' Fortunately I have learnt from my classes that art is subjective and everyone is free to interpret what they see as they choose (seriously, though, a SNAKE?????).

13th February

Daddy and Uncle Harry have spent a lot of today talking about a thing called Valentine's Day, which is where you have to buy presents for girls because otherwise they go mad and it's going to happen tomorrow.

'The question is,' Uncle Harry said, 'what do these aliens want? What do they actually like?'

'It's making my palms sweat just thinking about it,' Daddy said. 'What goes on in their minds? How are we supposed to keep track of their needs when no rules apply and they're free to change what they've said about everything with no warning?'

'I don't know what you're worried about – it's so easy for you this year,' Uncle Harry said. 'You don't need to bother with jewellery or flowers or naming an undiscovered planet after her. She'd be more than happy with a bargain bucket from KFC.'

'Obviously I'm getting her one of those,' Daddy said. 'But what if that's not romantic enough?'

'Mate,' Uncle Harry said, 'throw in a six-pack of Tango and an Iceland Black Forest Cheesecake and she'll want to renew your wedding vows.'

14th February

Daddy surprised Mummy with breakfast in bed this morning. He brought her a tray with that KFC bargain bucket on it and the Black Forest Cheesecake, which he said was from me. She was so happy, she cried, and then she took photos of it.

'It's like you read my actual mind,' she said, sticking her face into the bucket and inhaling deeply.

'It doesn't end here,' Daddy said. 'Only the best for my girl.'

She had Krispy Kremes that had been especially baked into hearts for lunch, packets of Frazzles every hour all afternoon, Liquorice Allsorts at teatime and, Daddy told me as a secret, a Mighty Meat Pizza from Domino's for supper.

I didn't do badly out of Valentine's Day either. As in, I got sent over a thousand cards, so that was nice.

15th February

Uncle Harry came for breakfast today. When Mummy asked if she could have another pizza instead of her usual superfood smoothie, Uncle Harry turned to Daddy and said, 'Do you ever worry that she's literally going to end up going through the bins?'

Little does he know she's been doing that since Hallowe'en.

16th February

Daddy has been with his Chinese and Japanese teachers all day because we're having China and Japan Week in advance of his trip. Not only can he now speak a bit of Chinese, he can also make an origami swan, which is so clever.

19th February

We saw Goonie and GaGa today after their visit to Chinatown and they told us all about it.

'I made dumplings and wrote in Chinese, and I don't mind saying I was awful at the former and awfully good at the latter,' GaGa said.

'They told us I was born in the Year of the Rat and Gladys was born in the Year of the Pig,' Goonie said. 'Isn't it marvellous?'

'You like cheese and I like truffles,' GaGa said, 'so it's also terribly accurate.'

Then they hugged each other, which was a bit embarrassing but also quite nice in a weird way.

25th February

こんにちは

That's Japanese for 'hello'.

Daddy is in Japan. On our Skype call he said he drank a lot of tea in a special tea ceremony today. It sounds different from teatime at home, because they didn't give him any biscuits.

I'm really hoping this news doesn't reach David. It might cause an international incident.

26th February

Daddy says he is starving. He can't use chopsticks, so he has barely been able to eat since he arrived in Japan. He says he drops absolutely everything he tries to pick up, usually in the soy sauce, which then splashes everywhere, but he's too embarrassed to ask for a fork.

'Luckily I found this packet of peas in the minibar,' he told us tonight on the Skype call, 'so I'm just going to have those, even though they're cold.' He opened the packet and started eating.

'How was your day, George?' he asked, munching on a big handful. 'Wow, these are crunchier than I was expecting.'

Mummy started telling him what we'd been doing.

Daddy's face got pinker and pinker. 'Are you all right?' Mummy asked. 'You look like you're sweating.'

Daddy started to cough. 'Bloody hell, what's the matter with these peas?' He loosened his tie and looked at the packet. 'What does wassaby mean?' He held up the packet for Mummy to see.

'Wasabi,' Mummy said. 'It's Japanese horseradish. That packet says it's extra hot.'

'Water,' Daddy croaked, snatching some flowers out of a vase and drinking straight from it.

27th February

Daddy was asked to try on a whole Samurai costume today at a film studio in Tokyo. Including the helmet. 'I looked like such an arse,' he said on his Skype call.

'If it's any consolation,' Mummy said, 'Dad is literally beside himself with jealousy.'

'Please don't let Spike see the photographs,' Daddy said.

'About that . . .' Mummy said.

'Oh God, don't tell me he has already?' Daddy put his face in his hands.

'He might have done,' Mummy said.

Daddy's mobile beeped. 'Oh here we go. It's from him,' Daddy said. '"Wombat-san",' he read aloud. '"Will you paint my fence when you get home?"'

Mummy started to laugh.

' "And then will you sand my floors and wax my car?" *The Karate Kid* isn't even about a Samurai Warrior. This is not a funny joke.'

'I don't know why he doesn't pay more attention to getting his cultural references right,' Mummy said. 'Anyone would think he only cares about taking the piss out of you.'

March 2015

2nd March

你好

That's Chinese for 'hello'.

Daddy is now in Beijing. He got to play football today and go round a place called the Forbidden City, which was built about six hundred years ago. Uncle Harry says G-Pop went to the housewarming they had for it.

3rd March

We went to visit GG and G-Pop at HQ towards the end of the day today. They were getting ready for the Mexican State Banquet. GG came out of her dressing room wearing a large sombrero and one of those fake moustaches from Christmas. 'Can I get away with it, do you think?' she asked Mummy. But then she took them off and put on a tiara and a huge diamond necklace instead.

'I've said I'll give her a pound if she sneaks this tequila worm into the President's drink,' G-Pop said, holding out a small worm in the palm of his hand.

'The easiest pound I shall ever earn,' GG said.

'Cocky!' G-Pop said. And they both hooted with laughter.

'Going to fill up on shepherd's pie before tonight,' G-Pop went on. 'In case someone tries to make me eat a taco.'

4th March

Daddy gave a speech today about the illegal wildlife trade at the Botanical Gardens in Xishuangbanna and then he fed carrots to an elephant called Ran-Ran.

'I wish I'd been able to wear some Tuskcember tusks,' Daddy told Mummy, on the Skype call. 'It's so mysterious that the designs for them vanished.'

'I know. I wonder how that happened,' Mummy said neutrally.

'Any luck finding them?' Daddy asked.

'No, not yet,' Mummy said. 'But we'll keep looking.'

After the call, Mummy pulled a large hardback envelope out from under the sofa and gave it to her Private Secretary. 'These need to be "disappeared". Know what I'm saying?'

'Of course,' her Private Secretary replied.

'And we never had this conversation,' Mummy said, tapping her nose.

'What conversation?' her Private Secretary said.

'I'm glad we understand each other,' Mummy said, reaching for her bag of jumbo-sized marshmallows.

7th March

Daddy is back from his trip. He bought Mummy an embroidered silk kimono, me a huge toy panda and Uncle Harry a Samurai wig. It has a lot of hair at the back but is bald at the front. Uncle Harry has been wearing it all day. He looks like the spitting image of Great Uncle Eddie – but with more hair.

'I feel like I could chop a wall in half with my bare hands,' Uncle Harry said, rubbing the bald part at the front.

'Told you,' Daddy replied. 'Less hair, more power.'

9th March

Happy Commonwealth Day!

Mummy and Daddy went to the Commonwealth Day Observance at Westminster Abbey today. Goonie and GaGa were there and so were GG and G-Pop, but I had to stay behind for the stupid Sibling Rivalry class.

Ringo the plastic baby apparently wanted to play football with me, which was ridiculous because it didn't look like the kind of plastic baby that knows how to kick a ball.

The Sibling Rivalry Coach moved one of Plastic Ringo's plastic legs to make it stick out, then bashed it against the football, saying, 'Passing it to you, George.'

It was the worst game of football I have ever played. Worse than the time I played with Great Aunt Annie, who cried when she missed her penalty, so that's saying something.

12th March

Mummy went to the set of *Downton Abbey* today. Everyone was SO jealous. She came back with a wooden train for me from the George character in the story. She says he is the one who is only going to inherit an Earldom, poor thing.

'Did they tell you anything??' Daddy asked desperately, when she got home.

'I watched some of the filming, yes,' Mummy said.

'Tell me Isis is actually OK and it was all just a dream?' Daddy said.

'You don't have the clearance, I'm afraid,' Mummy said.

'What about Lady Mary?' Daddy asked. 'Does she go on to marry that handsome chap from the Christmas special?'

'Maybe she does,' Mummy said. 'Maybe she doesn't.'

'Just reassure me that Edith isn't going to end up alone,' Daddy said.

'I *could* tell you that,' Mummy said. 'But then I'd have to kill you.'

13th March

You wouldn't think such a thing were possible, but Mummy's hair is getting thicker and thicker.

'Where is it all coming from?' Daddy asked her today, as her Hair Team were heaving it around to try to put it up for the Afghanistan service at St Paul's. 'I turn my back and five minutes later there's more of it. She won't be able to fit through the door soon.'

'Can someone get me some frozen peas for my neck?' Mummy asked. 'It's getting volcanic under there.'

17th March

Happy St Patrick's Day!

Mummy and Daddy visited the Irish Guards today and gave everybody shamrocks – even the regiment's dog. Daddy had a big bunch of it stuck to his cap, like he'd fallen into a bush.

In other news, Uncle Harry has announced that he's going to leave the army.

'Oh, good. We can take that ad for a new house-keeper out of the *Lady*,' Mummy said to him, when he came for tea today. 'When can you start?'

20th March

Mummy, Daddy and Uncle Harry have been talking about names for Ringo because so far in the history of the Royal Family, there hasn't been a Prince or Princess Ringo and that means they have to have back-up options.

'Alice or Richard?' Daddy said.

'Kim or Kanye?' Mummy said.

'Well, seeing as it currently looks like something out of *Alien*,' Uncle Harry said, 'what about Ripley or Newt?'

'Fantine or Jean Valjean?' Daddy said.

Mummy started Googling baby names on her iPhone. 'What about something from *Game of Thrones*? They're very popular at the moment. Daenerys or Tyrion or Jon Snow?' she said. 'Then HBO might let us in on future plot lines.'

'Dracarys after one of Khaleesi's dragons?' Uncle Harry said.

'There are dragons in *Game of Thrones*?' Daddy asked, sounding surprised.

'You know nothing, Prince William,' Mummy said in a wistful voice.

'If you didn't spend every episode with your back turned and a cushion over your face shouting, "What's happening? What's happening?" you'd know that,' Uncle Harry said.

'But it's so brutal,' Daddy said.

'Brutal and BRILLIANT,' Uncle Harry said. 'I still miss Sean Bean, though.'

'Why? What happened to him?' Daddy asked.

'His character left the North to go on a barging holiday in South Wales,' Uncle Harry said, smirking. He looked at Mummy and they started laughing.

'And then he decided to give up being Hand of the King and become a Club Med rep in Portugal,' she added. 'That show is full of surprises.'

'Probably a good idea,' Daddy said. 'I didn't like the way things were going with him and that Jeffrey fellow.'

'Joffrey,' Mummy said.

'This is what I'm talking about,' Daddy said. 'Can't trust a guy who doesn't even know how to spell his own name.'

25th March

'I know I said no wheat,' David said in his meeting with GG today, 'but I forgot that would mean no pasta too and, to be honest, I'm finding that a total nightmare.'

'Impossible to imagine one's life without pasta,' GG said sympathetically.

'And another thing. I hate running,' David said as he picked up a sandwich. 'How many calories are there in a cucumber?'

'I'm afraid I haven't the least idea,' GG said.

'George would know,' David said archly. 'He's doing the 5:2.'

'I've heard that's rather hard,' GG said.

'For most people it is,' David said. 'But not George. It's all, "I feel so energized" and "the weight is falling off" and "someone give me a Mars Bar before I fade away into thin air".'

'Frustrating when that happens,' GG said. 'Some people just find it easier, I suppose.'

'All that stuff last week about working to reduce the size of the enormous national debt through austerity measures,' David said, 'I know what he was really saying.'

'What was that?' GG asked.

'Well, it's obvious, isn't it?' David said morosely.

'Is it?' GG asked.

'Yes,' David said. 'It was a dig at me. How I'm not being "austere" enough to reduce my own "enormous national debt".' He patted his stomach. 'You can accuse George of a lot of things but subtlety is not one of them.'

'Indeed,' GG said. 'And now, perhaps we might turn our attention to the National Living Wage?'

'What if I only ate the cucumber?' David said, opening one of the sandwiches. 'It's basically just water, isn't it?'

When we got home, Daddy came bursting through the door, shouting 'They're going to stop making *Downton*!'

'I already knew that,' Mummy said.

'You didn't say anything!' Daddy said.

'I had to sign a piece of paper saying I'd give them George if I did,' Mummy said.

'And Wayne has left One Direction!'

'It's Zayn,' Mummy said. 'And I don't want to talk about it.'

'Not him as well?' Daddy said. 'Crikey, there'll be no one left at this rate.'

Later, Mummy stuck a picture of One Direction still including Zayn on the fridge. She then got out a pen and wrote 'When the world made sense' across the top of it.

26th March

Goonie and GaGa came for lunch today. Goonie was in a fluster because he wrote some private letters to the government a long time ago and now the law says they can be published for everyone to see.

'I was only trying to be helpful. Ragwort is a poisonous weed that needs to be kept under control,' Goonie said, sounding frustrated. 'Do most people know that? I don't think so.'

'They will now!' GaGa said, winking at Mummy.

'And then there are all those lovely historic buildings going to rack and ruin,' Goonie went on. 'It's enough to make one weep.'

'Chillax, dramavore,' GaGa said.

That cheered Goonie up a lot. 'No idea what that means,' he said, beaming at Daddy, 'but I like it. Isn't she wonderful?'

30th March

GG dissolved Parliament today. That is because we're having a thing called the General Election where everyone draws a cross on a piece of paper next to the name of the person they like the most. This is called democracy and it's terribly important.

We in the fam are not allowed to say who we want. We have to let everyone else decide and then GG asks the captain of the winning team if they want to form a government. I learnt this in my Politics and the Constitution class today.

I wonder if David is excited or scared. Perhaps he doesn't want the same job again. Or perhaps he would miss us and GG's lemon biscuits.

In other news, Daddy started his air ambulance training today. Uncle Harry and Mummy gave him a present to wish him luck. It was a remote-control helicopter and he flew it straight into a bush.

April 2015

1st April

Mummy went for a scan at the hospital today so she could check on Ringo. She came back looking very serious and said she needed to tell us something.

'I have news,' she said, solemnly. 'And it's important that you stay calm.'

Daddy gulped. 'Why am I now not feeling at all calm?'

'It's good news,' Mummy said. 'Just rather ... unexpected.'

'Wait,' Uncle Harry said. 'Has Zayn decided to rejoin One Direction?'

'Has Julian Fellowes decided to keep writing *Downton Abbey*?' Daddy asked.

'No,' Mummy said. 'Something else.'

'Well, come on then, Fatty, what is it?' Uncle Harry said.

'I'm expecting twins,' Mummy said.

There was total silence.

'*Twins?*' Daddy croaked, in a strange, high-pitched whisper.

'Yup,' Mummy said.

'Double trouble!' Uncle Harry shouted. 'I love it!'

'How? How? How?' Daddy gasped. 'I mean – *how*?'

'Well, I don't know, do I?' Mummy said. 'I'm as shocked as you are.'

'Put your hands up if you're a father of three!' Uncle Harry cheered.

'Oh my God,' Daddy whispered. 'We've got so much to do – we need to get another team hired, we need to speak to our Press Secretaries, we need to tell the family, we need to get Granny's approval.' He got up and started pacing the room.

'I've even thought of names for them,' Mummy said.

'Have you?' Daddy said hysterically. 'What?'

'April,' Mummy said, 'and Fool.'

And then she and Uncle Harry fell about laughing and high-fiving each other.

'That was brilliant!' Uncle Harry said. 'Your face, Wombat!'

'You owe me a fiver,' Mummy said. Uncle Harry got his wallet out as Daddy collapsed into a chair with his face in his hands.

'OK, that was good,' he said. 'Genuinely hilarious. It may not look like it, but I'm laughing on the inside.'

That was NOT funny.

3rd April

Today is a day called Good Friday. A long time ago, Jesus, the one from Christmas, died on the cross. I learnt that in Easter class today.

The thing is, if Good Friday is the day that he died, then why is it good? I think it should be changed to Horrible Friday. If a person is going to die to save mankind, the least we could do is make it sound less cheerful.

4th April

We are at Goonie and GaGa's. Tomorrow we get to eat chocolate ALL DAY! Mummy is literally counting the hours. Me too!!!

5th April

Today is a day called Easter Sunday. A long time ago, Jesus, the one from Christmas and Good Friday, rose from the dead and felt better so he went to heaven. I also learnt that in Easter class.

There are a few things I don't get, though. What does rising from the dead have to do with eating chocolate eggs? And that cross he died on – how did it end up on a bun?

Also, where did the Easter Bunny come from? Did Jesus have a pet bunny? Where does it get all the eggs? Bunnies don't even lay actual eggs, let alone chocolate ones.

Not that I'm complaining because Easter is BRILLIANT!

We had our Easter-egg hunt in Goonie and GaGa's garden and it was totally ace. The dogs had to be kept indoors, which drove them completely mad. Lupo can barely look me in the eye. Beth and Bluebell keep growling at GaGa – but who cares when you are allowed to eat chocolate instead of kale? LOL.

Mummy helped me during the hunt by holding my basket and pointing out the eggs I missed, but I feel like I ended up with less than I thought I'd found. That may or may not have had something to do with her saying, 'one for Georgie, one for Mummy,' and then munching down every second egg we found. By the end of the day, she had pretty much stopped speaking. When Daddy asked her a question, she said, 'This is valuable eating time. Don't distract me until I give you some kind of non-verbal sign that I've finished.'

The most charming thing of all was that the Easter eggs were all Duchy Originals. It's so thoughtful of the Easter Bunny.

6th April

Today is Easter Monday. Which is the day that Jesus felt really sick from eating all the eggs. We do too.

8th April

People are placing bets on what Ringo's name is going to be. No one has thought of Daenerys or Tyrion, but lots of people have thought of Alice or Richard. Uncle Harry is trying to claim that GG has endorsed his number-one choice, 'Newt'. No one is falling for it.

Instead, Mummy and Daddy spent some time writing lists of who they could ask to be godparents this afternoon and when they'd finished, they swapped.

'Jay Z?' Mummy sighed. 'Not this again. We met him once. For five minutes.'

'He might say yes.'

'He is not going to say yes,' Mummy said. 'And do you know why? Because we're not going to ask him.'

'I just felt –'

'No, you didn't,' Mummy said. 'You did not feel a connection.'

Daddy looked at Mummy's list. 'Zayn from One Direction?'

'The responsibility might help him refocus for the future,' Mummy said.

'That's a good point,' Daddy said. 'But the tattoos worry me a bit.'

He paused. 'Let's put him on the "maybe" list.'

Mummy turned back to Daddy's list. 'Who's Ran-Ran?'

'That elephant I fed carrots to in China,' Daddy said excitedly. 'Wouldn't that be *amazing*?'

'Yes. If we were in *The Jungle Book*,' Mummy said. 'But we're not. We're in Kensington.'

'Think of the cultural diversity,' Daddy said. 'Plus Ran-Ran would never forget Christmas or birthdays.'

'True,' Mummy said. 'And she also wouldn't be able to get on a plane and be here for the christening. Because she is an elephant.'

'That would be such a shame,' Daddy said.

'There are many things it would be,' Mummy said, 'and "a shame" is quite low among them.'

Daddy looked at Mummy's list again. 'Harry from One Direction,' he read aloud.

'A moral guardian if ever there was one.'

'Louis from One Direction.'

'Remember how much you liked his hair?'

'Liam from One Direction.'

'He seems like a very sensible person to me.'

'The other one from One Direction.'

'You know who I mean – thingy – the blond one.'

Daddy thought about it. 'OK,' he said brightly. 'Let's put them on the "maybe" list too. Just above Claudia Winkleman.'

9th April

Goonie and GaGa have been married for ten years today! Ten years. That is an eternity. Apparently it is traditional to give each other a present made of tin, so GaGa gave Goonie a tin watering can and Goonie gave GaGa a tin bee smoker. They are both THRILLED.

12th April

Mummy has started acting a bit weirdly again.

She keeps tidying up. Usually our housekeepers manage all that stuff, but Mummy is now tidying after they've tidied. She says she can't stop herself.

'She's nesting,' Daddy told Uncle Harry and me. 'Which means it won't be long until Ringo is here.'

'Couldn't swing her by my jumper drawer, could you?' Uncle Harry said. 'And my car, because that's in a total state too. I haven't cleaned it for ages.'

'I'll ask her,' Daddy said. 'When she's finished hoovering the hoover.'

14th April

Mummy took everything out of the fridge today, cleaned it, put everything back – then did the whole thing again an hour later. 'In case I missed a spot,' she said.

'The fridge is cleaned regularly, Ma'am,' the Kitchen Team said.

'Of course,' Mummy said, scrubbing the vegetable drawers. 'You always do an excellent job. I have no idea what I'm doing – but the urge is overwhelming.'

'Yes, Ma'am,' the Head Chef said. 'Perhaps we might suggest wearing these Marigolds.'

A huge smile broke out across Mummy's face. 'Heaven,' she said, putting on the pair of bright yellow rubber gloves. 'I might wear them to Ascot this year.'

15th April

It's Uncle J's birthday today! He is TWENTY-EIGHT!!! Listen to those bones creak! He came round this afternoon with a cake he'd baked himself (he doesn't like anyone else doing it for him) and a box of marshmallows with his face on them, which he'd designed for all of us. He is so sweet to give other people presents on his own birthday. Mummy stopped cleaning for a whole hour to celebrate – although maybe it would have been better if she had waited until everyone had actually finished tea before starting to tidy up their plates.

16th April

Woken at 3.30 a.m. this morning by Mummy going through my cupboard.

'Sorry, Georgie,' she said. 'Go back to sleep. Mummy just needs to organize your shirts. For the third time.'

I left her to it.

19th April

Mummy is completely exhausted. She keeps waking up in the night and emptying entire cupboards and then not going back to bed until everything has been cleaned and put back in a specific order.

'I thought I'd organize the DVDs alphabetically,' she said this morning, 'but then I took them all out and organized them by colour. Then I took them all out *again* and organized them by date. But then that didn't work, so I alphabetized them again.'

'I think they were already alphabetized, Babykins,' Daddy said gently.

'Aha,' Mummy said, 'but had they all been individually cleaned first? I don't think so.'

She's dusting frantically today. Even though there is no dust.

21st April

Happy Birthday, GG! She is EIGHTY-NINE years old today!!! That's the same as a million Uncle Harrys!

GG doesn't like to make a fuss for her birthday. It was just a low-key affair with a 41-gun salute in Green Park, a 21-gun salute in Windsor Great Park and a 62-gun salute at the Tower of London. I'd be amazed if anyone even noticed.

25th April

Mummy is getting more and more tired these days. She says Ringo is feeling very heavy and uncomfortable. All she wants to do is sleep and clean cupboards. Her excess hair is now so heavy that Daddy has to push her head off the pillow in the morning because she is struggling to lift it herself.

She has started drinking something called Raspberry Leaf Tea. Apparently it will wake lazy old Ringo up and get it moving.

Feeling nervous . . .

27th April

Ringo's room is ready and waiting. I'm trying to picture it in that cot, staring at the lions-and-unicorns mobile. Uncle Harry is off to Australia soon and he's feeling a bit sad that he might miss the birth.

'I thought Ringo would be here by now,' he said to Mummy today. 'You need to get your groove on and pop before I leave the country.'

'All right,' Mummy said, looking at her enormous stomach. 'Go and get me a pin. Let's just burst this thing and get it over with.'

29th April

Today is Mummy and Daddy's fourth wedding anniversary. They watched their wedding video today to celebrate, i.e., the BBC coverage.

They were both very cheerful and we found them dancing around in the drawing room to a song called 'You're The One That I Want', which they had at their wedding reception. They were singing it to each other and pointing. It was so embarrassing.

'Get a room,' Uncle Harry said.

May 2015

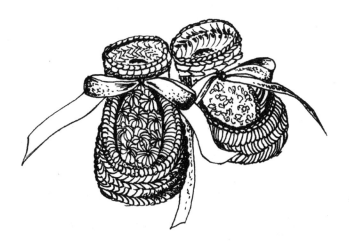

1st May

We went swimming at HQ yesterday and then we went with Daddy again today. Apparently it might help give Ringo the nudge.

I wish Ringo would just stay put. Things are fine as they are.

Mummy spent the rest of the day rubbing her back because she said it was really aching. She sat on her big bouncy ball, listening to her iPod and repeating things like 'Labour cannot be stronger than me because it IS me' and 'I am perfectly in sync with nature. I allow the rhythm of life to flow through me.'

'This could be it,' Daddy said to me.

Everyone's been saying that for ages, but Ringo is still not here.

2nd May

RINGO IS HERE. And it's a she.

This is so weird.

When I woke up, Mummy and Daddy weren't at home. The whole house was completely mental, so I knew something was up.

They sat me down after breakfast and told me the news.

'Mummy and Daddy are at the hospital because Mummy has just had the baby. Ringo has arrived and she's a girl – you have a little sister!' my Press Secretary said.

They all stared at me. But there wasn't time for pleasantries. We had to talk strategy.

Daddy rang from the hospital to say he was going to come and collect me, so we knew it was going to be a big day for the press.

'Let's go hard with the blue,' my stylist said. 'There'll be so much pink around today, it'll work strongly as a contrast.'

My Wardrobe Team consulted on various options. We decided on a white shirt, cardigan, shorts and long socks. Clean, classic and co-ordinated with Daddy, they said, but with my own stamp.

Hair – simple, side-parting. A light trim.

My Mood Analyst and Movement Interpreter talked

about the press call with my Press Secretary and head of Global Strategy.

'I suggest you walk in,' my Movement Interpreter said to me. 'It shows independence, confidence and ability. Yes, there is a new baby here, but who is heir to the throne?'

'And smile,' my Mood Analyst said. 'In a nothing-about-this-worries-me way.'

'Your fans will love it,' my Press Secretary said. 'It's Ringo's day, but that doesn't mean we take this lying down.'

My Press Secretary turned to my Wardrobe Team. 'Any intel on Ringo's hospital wardrobe exit strategy?'

'Not yet,' my stylist said. 'But we've been in touch with the Met Office and temperatures suggest a hat may come into play.'

My Sibling Rivalry Coach turned up and gave me that plastic Ringo to play with again. They all eyed me as I dragged it round for a bit by its foot and then tossed it to Lupo to carry in his mouth by the scruff of the neck.

'How nice that you want Ringo to be friends with Lupo,' my Sibling Rivalry Coach said, looking worried.

Daddy came to pick me up in the afternoon and we went to the hospital. His face was all bright and happy. He told me about Ringo on the way there.

'Your little sister is gorgeous,' he said. 'And Mummy was so brave and clever and amazing – she can't wait to see you.'

There were thousands of people waiting when we arrived at the hospital. When we got out of the car, they started to cheer and applaud. I decided to ditch the walking strategy – I thought a headshot of Daddy and me would be better, so I made him carry me.

The bank of press was pretty extensive, but nothing I wasn't prepared for.

'Let's give them a wave,' Daddy said. We waved a bit together. No smiling, though. I wanted to keep them guessing. It works for Victoria Beckham.

A quick over-the-shoulder shot as Daddy went into the hospital and that was enough.

Mummy was in a room having her hair done and I was relieved to see her. 'Hooray!' she said, and gave me a big hug. 'I missed you.'

There was a clear box in the corner with a small cone-shaped thing in it and they said that was Ringo. I sat on Mummy's lap and Daddy lifted Ringo up and held her on my lap so I could inspect her. I touched her face a bit. She didn't really do much. She just sort of lay there.

'This is your sister,' Mummy said. 'Look how tiny she is.'

She had only a bit of hair and she mewed like a strange cat-alien. Her face was a bit squashed – like she'd been kept under a pile of books. That was sort of it, really.

I went home after that and then Mummy and Daddy

came back with Ringo slumped in a car seat. It felt like everyone was talking about her. They turned Tower Bridge pink and the London Eye and the BT Tower and the Golden Jubilee Bridge. The Royal Navy stood in a special formation that spelt out 'SISTER' on HMS *Dragon*. Huge crowds of people gathered outside the railings of HQ to see the easel with the announcement of Ringo's birth on it. The TV coverage went on for hours and hours and hours.

GG was in Yorkshire today, but she wore pink and said she was thrilled. Goonie and GaGa said they were thrilled. Granny C and Grandpa M said they were thrilled. The Obamas said they were thrilled. The news was trending on Twitter all day around the world. Because apparently the world was thrilled. It was all a bit over the top if you ask me.

Ringo slept through all of it.

3rd May

Ringo is still here.

Mummy and Daddy looked exhausted this morning. When Ringo wakes up, they have to wake up too. And when Ringo is awake, she wants to drink milk so Mummy has to feed her. If she is not feeding within seconds, she immediately gets cross and makes her cat-alien noise. She drinks and drinks and then most of it looks like it just comes out of her mouth again and then she falls back asleep.

Goonie and GaGa came to see us today, and so did Granny C, Grandpa M and Aunt P. They are so excited that Ringo is a girl.

'A granddaughter! It's marvellous!' Goonie said.

'Isn't she sweet!' GaGa said.

'She looks like you when you were born!' Granny C said.

'I bought her this strawberry fancy-dress outfit!' Grandpa M said.

They brought her so many presents. This house is overrun with things that are PINK. Clothes, toys, balloons, flowers, Daddy's face. The doorbell rings every five minutes and another present arrives. Her Present Team are run off their feet.

I'm also doing quite well out of this brother lark. Ringo gave me an inflatable crocodile for my swimming class and some football goals for the garden. I'll admit they weren't bad presents – but I still can't work out how she had time to go shopping when she's only been here for a day.

They're still talking about names, so she might not end up being called Ringo after all.

'I know we can't,' Mummy said, 'but part of me wants to stick it to the bookies and call her Elaine or Chrysanthemum or Imperator Furiosa.'

Daddy was on the phone to GG.

'What do you think of Imperator Furiosa?' he asked GG. He smiled brightly and turned to Mummy. 'She says it does have a precedent. Apparently it's what they called Great Aunt Annie when she was little.'

There was a pause.

'OK, she says she was joking.'

'She should be called Perfect Angel Baby,' Mummy said, beaming at Ringo.

'What about Perfect Angel Baby?' Daddy asked. 'She says she thinks someone called Katie Price already has a daughter called that.'

There was another pause.

'OK, that was also a joke.'

Anyway, they've decided on Charlotte Elizabeth Diana.

Ringo is now called Charlotte. But obviously, because my family are obsessed with nicknames, she's already being referred to as Lotto. Like Lottie, but with an *o*. Because of Ringo.

Lotto herself doesn't seem to care about any of her new names. She slept through all of it.

4th May

My outfit from Saturday has sold out everywhere. Kid's still got it #GeorgeForTheWin

Oh – and the soldiers from the King's Troop Royal

Horse Artillery gave Lotto a 41-gun salute in Hyde Park, while the Honourable Artillery Company gave her a 62-gun salute at the Tower of London. She just yawned when Mummy told her.

5th May

Mummy is obsessed with Lotto. She stares at her all day. Sometimes she cries for no reason and says, 'I'm so happy.' And then she wants to give me a big hug and I get suffocated by her hair. It's now SO thick and generally huge in all ways that Daddy says it could almost become a country and join the UN.

Daddy permanently has muslins over his shoulders like a sous-chef. Lotto spends the whole time tightly bound like Tom Kitten that time he got caught by Samuel Whiskers and Anna Maria and they rolled him up in pastry. Like a sort of rugby ball with a head sticking out of the top.

GG came and visited today. She was really excited to meet Lotto and give her a present. 'This is just a little something from your great-grandmother, GG, darling,' GG said to Lotto. 'It's a diamond bracelet that used to belong to Queen Charlotte, my third great-grandmother. George III bought Buckingham Palace for her. Wasn't that sweet of him?'

The bracelet was quite shiny, I suppose. It made

Mummy cry. But a tea towel made Mummy cry earlier so that's not saying much.

'Nice to have a daughter.' GG sighed. 'They break fewer things, I find.'

Then I sat on GG's lap and she fixed my train because the back wheel had come off. She said it was the lug nut, and fastened it again with her miniature spanner. Now it's as good as new. Having a trained mechanic in the family is so handy.

Daddy went and filled out a form this afternoon and it means that Lotto is now a real person who exists in the law.

6th May

David was all over the shop in his meeting with GG today and it's because of that thing called the General Election.

'I mean, I can barely eat a morsel, I'm so nervous,' David said.

'Perhaps just some tea, then?' GG said. 'It's good for anxiety.'

'Nervous with excitement, I mean,' David said, not looking excited. 'I'm very confident that we'll get a majority. Very confident indeed.'

He rubbed his hands on his trousers and did not look confident.

'Is it me or is it quite hot in here?' he asked, loosening his tie.

'It is a little warm today,' GG said.

'I haven't weighed myself, but I bet I've lost several pounds. Maybe even quarter of a stone,' David said. 'No appetite at all at the moment.'

'I won't offer you a sandwich then,' GG said.

David bit his lip.

'Except it's important I keep my strength up though, isn't it?' David said. 'I'm going to have to pull an all-nighter tomorrow and I can't do that on an empty stomach.'

'True,' GG said. 'Fruitcake?'

'Only for my energy levels,' David said, holding his plate out.

We drove to Anmer this evening. I sat in the back with Lotto who stared at me and then let a load of milk she'd just drunk come gushing out of her mouth. Then she went to sleep. Scintillating company!

I'm finding her very hard to work out. Everyone seems to be besotted with her, but she literally doesn't do anything. She just lies there letting people tell her how marvellous she is. They don't even get a smile out of it.

She hasn't attempted to play with any of my toys yet, so she's perhaps cleverer than I first gave her credit for. Unless she's trying to lull me into a false sense of security. Arrgh, she's like that fox in *Jemima Puddleduck* – who can tell if she's acting or not???

Uncle Harry Skyped Mummy and Daddy last night and they held up Lotto for him to see. He was really excited – until she was sick all over the laptop and they said they'd have to stop the call.

'Ahh,' Uncle Harry said. 'Just like her mother.'

7th May

Today is the General Election. The day when the country decides whether David keeps his job or someone new gets it. Apparently the last time there was a general election it got very complicated and they ended up with a thing called a Hung Parliament. That's because you have to hang around for days until someone decides who the winner is. Uncle Harry told me that.

8th May

Everyone is saying there has been a landslide in Scotland! What does that mean? Have all the houses fallen down???

GG has gone rushing back to HQ because David is keeping his job and she has to ask him to form a government and get the kitchens working on a completely massive tea. Apparently someone called Paddy Ashdown now has to eat a hat on TV because of it. He should have promised to eat a whole cake if David kept his job. Not only would David have approved, he would have helped him.

Lotto does not seem interested in all this political intrigue. Fortunately for her, she doesn't have to be. I, on the other hand, have no choice because one day I will be asking people to form governments and talking to them about how to stop Scotland falling down in the night.

11th May

Uncle Harry is in New Zealand. He was wearing a feathered Maori cape when he Skyped us and he showed us a toy parrot he'd also been given as a present for Lotto. It's fine, because I didn't actually want a toy parrot, and even if I did, there's nothing Lotto can do to stop me playing with it because she can't move or hold anything in her hands, or say, 'Don't play with my toy parrot, George.' Also, when Mummy held her up to look at it, she just dribbled out of the side of her mouth, so I don't think she even knows it's hers.

Uncle Harry also said that he played in a pub quiz and his team, the Ginger Ninjas, came second.

He's always second. Like Lotto. Long may it stay that way.

12th May

Mummy and Daddy are obsessed with taking photos of Lotto. She has an iPhone in her face the entire time and there are now ten million photos of her either sleeping or with milk or dribble coming out of her mouth. Every time they take a picture, they go, 'Oooooh, look at her! She's so pretty!' as if she's done something remarkable or marvellous, then send it to someone. Uncle Harry is being bombarded with a constant stream of identical photos of her. It's literally like they've gone mad.

The strange thing is, I think Uncle Harry is being sucked into it all. He has confessed to a reporter that he would like to settle down and have children. I am not averse to this plan because the world could only be improved by having more Uncle Harrys in it – but, honestly, this baby-obsession is starting to become undignified.

16th May

What I don't understand is, if a baby sleeps all the time, why would its mummy and daddy be so tired? My energy levels are tip-top, but everyone else is dragging around the house yawning and saying how shattered they are. First they said I was exhausting because I never stop running around, and now they're saying Lotto is exhausting, but she's been lying down since she got here. Daddy has started falling asleep standing up, like a horse, and Mummy said she would do art class with me today but she ended up falling asleep on my picture of a parrot and now she's walking round with green paint in her hair.

18th May

Uncle Harry told a reporter in New Zealand yesterday that he loved the army so much he thinks Lotto and I should join it one day. That way, we won't become lay-abouts who constantly get into trouble. Lotto is definitely a layabout – but how much trouble can a person who is perpetually asleep really get into?

I wouldn't mind joining the army. You get to hide in trees and no one gets cross if you get mud on your clothes.

19th May

Uncle Harry is home and has come straight to Anmer to visit us. He came bounding in doing a thing called the Haka where you shout and fling your arms about and stick your tongue out.

'We've missed your classic dance moves,' Mummy said.

Uncle Harry brought all of us a cape made of traditional Maori textiles. I am wearing mine now. It's quite itchy and very long, but I really like it. Needless to say, Lotto has given no indication as to whether she likes hers or not.

Uncle Harry was intrigued to meet her. He picked her up and inspected her closely. 'Squeaky little thing, isn't she?' he said. 'Small, like a gerbil, but less furry.' He sniffed her head. 'Milky,' he said. 'Yes. I approve of this child. I approve immensely. You may keep her.'

'That's a relief,' Mummy said, 'because for the life of me I can't find the receipt anywhere.'

Uncle Harry held Lotto up so they were face to face.

'Hello. I am your Uncle Harry,' he said. 'What's your story?'

Lotto stared at him and said nothing.

'Slow down, I can't understand everything you're saying,' Uncle Harry said.

Lotto yawned.

'I know,' Uncle Harry said. 'I really need to work on my conversational skills.'

Then she fell asleep.

Uncle Harry gave her back to Mummy and we went off to have an excellent afternoon playing 'What's the Time, Mr Wolf?' in the garden. And then we found snails together, but we didn't tell Mummy because

Uncle Harry said she would prefer it if we just put one on her plate at teatime as a surprise.

He was right. She was surprised. So surprised in fact that she shouted a whole load of strange words I'd never heard before.

20th May

Mummy took some photos of Lotto and me together today. Not on her iPhone, but on the camera she has that I'm not allowed to touch. And they're not just for Granny C, Aunt P and Uncle Harry – they're for the whole world.

For the past week, my team have been working like fiends on wardrobe strategy and my proposed look, and we had a meeting about it prior to the shoot. With Lotto's team. They sat on one side of the conference table, while my team sat on the other.

'We're thinking white,' Lotto's stylist said.

'We're thinking white too,' my stylist replied.

There was a pause. They sized each other up across the table.

'Good,' Lotto's stylist said. 'Nice and co-ordinated then.'

'But,' my stylist said, 'we'll be adding blue.'

There was another pause. Lotto's team looked at each other.

'Fine with us,' Lotto's stylist said. 'Better, in fact.'

'Good,' my stylist said.

'Good,' Lotto's stylist said.

'Hair?' Lotto's Hairdresser said.

'Side-parting,' my Hairdresser replied rigidly. 'You?'

'Well . . .' Lotto's Hairdresser said '. . . the Princess only has two weeks' growth.'

'Of course,' my Hairdresser said, unable to hide his smile.

'Then perhaps we can conclude this meeting,' my Press Secretary said. 'We'll meet you in the drawing room.'

Everyone got up and stiffly shook hands. I was taken out of my high chair, where I'd been playing with my animal skittles, and immediately to a fitting.

An hour later, we were all in the drawing room. Me in a crisp white shirt with a blue trim, blue shorts and blue long socks, and Lotto all in white.

'Let's put them on the sofa,' Mummy said.

I got onto the sofa and they put Lotto on my lap, propping her up with a load of pillows. She wriggled a bit, but not much. Between you and me, I think she might have the family instinct for what makes a good photo. Not that there isn't still A LOT she could learn from me.

Mummy directed us in the shoot, while everyone stood behind her and watched.

'Let's have a cheerful one,' Mummy said, from

behind the camera. Everyone started jumping up and down, waving their hands and making funny faces at me.

I laughed. Shot one.

'What about something contemplative, Ma'am?' My Mood Analyst said to Mummy.

'Georgie,' Mummy said, turning to me, 'what face would you make if I asked you to wear a kilt to save Scotland?'

Serious face. Shot two.

'Let's see those cute hands, Lotto,' Mummy said.

I looked at Lotto. She held up her hands and wriggled her fingers. Shot three.

'What about a brotherly kiss?' Lotto's Mood Analyst suggested.

'Good idea,' Mummy said. 'Georgie? Imagine Lotto was a crocodile.'

I gave her a kiss on her head. Shot four.

'That's a wrap!' Mummy said. 'Good work, everyone. Especially my flawless models.'

The whole room erupted into applause.

It went well, I feel. And I'll admit Lotto did better than expected for her first photo session. Our teams congratulated each other on a job well done, but we all know they'll be scouring the newspapers to see who gets the most coverage when these come out.

21st May

We are now in London. Daddy had his first appointments today since Lotto was born, which were meeting the Women's England Football team (it WOULD be cool if Lotto ended up playing for them), then holding some investitures at HQ.

'I told this really nice musician I gave an MBE to how I play bass guitar and now I've been asked to join a band called Aswad,' Daddy told us.

'I'm sorry – you said you "play bass guitar"?' Mummy asked, putting Lotto over her shoulder and rubbing her back. 'Since when?'

'Since, like, ages ago,' Daddy said. 'Remember how I used to play you songs at university?'

'On a plastic guitar you stole from a freshers' week party,' Mummy said. 'How that got translated into you being good at bass, I have no idea.'

'One guitar is much like another, isn't it?' Daddy said. 'Or isn't it?'

'I don't know, Karaoke Boy – why don't you ask your pal Jon Bon Jovi?' Mummy said, breaking into a large smile. She then started singing about someone called Tommy working on a dock in a sort of strained, gravelly voice and shaking her head around.

Daddy went a bit pink. 'Look, that was for charity,' he said. 'How was I supposed to know he'd make me go on stage? And who knows all the lyrics to "Livin' On A Prayer" anyway? Thank God for Taylor Swift – if she hadn't come on stage with me and whispered all the words, I might have been totally humiliated.'

Mummy burst out laughing. 'What a lucky escape,' she said.

Lotto then spewed down Mummy's back.

'That's my girl,' Daddy said, taking Lotto from Mummy as she took her cardigan off. 'Sticking up for Daddy.'

'You mean *sicking* up for Daddy,' Mummy said, wiping Lotto's chin. 'Perhaps you can play her a lullaby on your bass guitar.'

' "*Rock*abye Baby"?' Daddy said.

Then they both had hysterics and sang Lotto and me 'Rockabye Baby' in stupid rock voices, jumping around the room and punching the air. I was so embarrassed, I hid behind the sofa. If Taylor Swift had been there, she would have joined me.

23rd May

I have decided that, as Lotto keeps waking up in the night, it's only fair that I wake up too because otherwise she would get to see Mummy and Daddy more than I do.

For some strange reason, Mummy and Daddy don't seem to be on board with my plan. In fact, when I'd woken up for the third time, Daddy crawled into my room on his hands and knees and ended up just going to sleep on the floor next to my cot. I threw my bilby at him to wake him up, but he didn't even flinch. It seemed to do the trick when I threw my train, though.

Lotto tried to challenge me by repeatedly making her cat-alien noise. I heard Mummy saying, in a very tired voice, 'If you go to sleep, I'll give you a million pounds,' but it didn't seem to work.

25th May

Daddy fell asleep talking to Uncle Harry on the phone today and Mummy actually walked into a wall, but I feel fine. Even Lotto looks quite perky for once.

27th May

Today is the State Opening of Parliament. GG is the Head of State, which means she has to put on a long dress and cape and wear the Imperial State Crown to formally open a new session of Parliament. Did you know that crown weighs nearly two pounds and is so grand that it has its own carriage to travel to Parliament separately from GG? How's that for high maintenance?

The State Opening of Parliament has some really

fun traditions, like the Yeomen of the Guard searching the cellars in case Guy Fawkes, the one from Fireworks Night, has come back to life and is up to his old tricks again, trying to blow everybody up.

They also have to send a pretend hostage to HQ to make sure the monarch – as in GG – comes home in one piece. This year, it's the Vice Chamberlain who gets to be the fake hostage. He must be so excited! Some people have all the luck.

GG and G-Pop roll along to Parliament in the Diamond Jubilee State Coach, and before the ceremony starts, a fellow called Black Rod gets a door slammed in his face, but then they just open it again and everyone goes in. They should let me slam that door because I would be brilliant at it. That's going in my Notes for the Top Job book.

The other tradition that most people don't know about is the one where G-Pop hides GG's glasses for LOLZ. She needs them to read her speech from her throne about the government's plans. The game is, she has until the procession starts to find them, and if she doesn't succeed, she has to give up and G-Pop is allowed to set the menu for a week. If GG wins, the Mean Girls are allowed to sleep on the bed for a week.

This year he managed to slip them into Black Rod's frock-coat pocket and GG became totally frantic until she noticed Black Rod was blushing with guilt and busted him. G-Pop is obviously livid.

GG doesn't seem to get nervous about these things. She says as long as she has that stone with her, she knows she'll be fine.

I wonder what that means . . .

28th May

Daddy's football team has made it to the final of the FA Cup and he is completely hysterical about it. He has been wearing his Aston Villa T-shirt under his shirt every day and keeps singing the team song because he says it will bring them luck.

'Not that song again,' Uncle Harry said this evening. 'I'm losing the will to live.'

'If he sings it one more time, I might have to kill you,' Mummy said.

'I wish you would,' Uncle Harry said. 'Here, use this fork.'

29th May

Lotto slept through the night. Apparently this is some huge deal. Mummy and Daddy are ecstatic. It even stopped Daddy talking about Aston Villa for a whole ten minutes.

30th May

Today is the day. Daddy went to see Aston Villa play Arsenal in the FA Cup Final.

'We can do it!' he shouted before he left. 'This is our time! We are unstoppable! Come on, you Villans!'

Arsenal won 4–0.

'I can't talk about it,' Daddy said, when he got back. 'Never mention Aston Villa to me again.'

'I have never been more on board with a plan in my life,' Mummy replied.

She is always very supportive.

June 2015

2nd June

When GaGa came for supper this evening, she told us about a party she went to at HQ today to celebrate a hundred years of a thing called the Women's Institute. The Women's Institute is a club for girls. No boys allowed.

'I say, wouldn't it be marvellous if we did our own naked charity calendar like they did – you'd be up for it, wouldn't you, Kate? Nothing but a strategically placed sceptre and orb and a nice big smile? I'm sure I can strong-arm Annie and Soph into it as well.'

To say Mummy looked startled is an understatement.

GaGa roared with laughter. 'JOKES!' she guffawed, taking a picture of Mummy's horrified face on her iPhone. 'That's going on the fridge by the way.'

4th June

The WI parties continue. Today GG went to the Albert Hall, which I think we own because apparently it's royal, and ate a big cake with the WI members. THEY get to have cake two days in a row. Girls have all the luck.

GG also made Uncle Harry a Knight Commander of the Royal Victorian Order at HQ. It's a nice present that GG gives people when they've served her well.

'I didn't intentionally become the favourite grandson,' Uncle Harry said, looking at his badge, 'but I think we all knew it was inevitable.'

'I already have one of those, actually,' Daddy said. 'You do know I paid her to give you one too.'

'She told me you'd say that,' Uncle Harry replied. 'She said, "William has always been incredibly jealous of you and that's the only reason he got one first." '

'She told me she was going to say that,' Daddy said. 'We decided together that that's what she'd say.'

'She told me she'd told you that,' Uncle Harry said.

'She told me she was going to tell you that she'd told me that,' Daddy said.

'You're pathetic,' Uncle Harry said.

'And you're ginger,' Daddy said.

Then Uncle Harry just decided to get Daddy in

a headlock and rub his knuckle on Daddy's skull until he agreed to say, 'My name is Willy the Wombat and I am not the favourite. In fact, I'm sixth after the dogs.'

5th June

Lotto's christening details were announced to the press today. Mummy and Daddy still haven't decided on godparents and the debate continues. Mummy has suggested the girl from that show she loves – Kim Kardashian.

'George and North are very close in age,' Mummy said. 'And Kim and Kanye's second baby won't be that much younger than Lotto. It makes sense. Think of the free trainers we'd get from Kanye.'

Daddy said he wasn't sure – until Mummy reminded him that Kanye is very good friends with Jay Z and now Kim Kardashian is in their top five. Between Mel and Sue.

Lotto's christening is not going to be a grand affair. Just a small ceremony at St Mary Magdalene Church on the Sandringham estate with the man in the dress who sprinkles the water. You know, the Archbishop of Canterbury.

7th June

Another press day – but, though I say it myself, a significantly larger one. Those photos Mummy took of Lotto and me were released to the world. We discussed their reception in our team debrief.

'One word,' my head of Global Strategy said. 'Sensational.'

Everyone applauded.

'The world is even more in love with you,' my Media Manager said. 'If that were possible. Which it literally isn't – and yet somehow you've achieved it.'

'They're all desperately trying to interpret what you're thinking, Sir,' my Mood Analyst said. 'You're the Kate Moss of toddlers.'

Everyone roared with laughter. It made me so excited, I threw my tractor.

'We must acknowledge that Princess Charlotte was also very well received,' my Press Secretary said soberly. 'But let's face it – this is not a double act yet.'

They all turned to me.

'It's a one-man show.'

Applause and cheering.

Lotto's team tried to talk her through our global smash, but as usual she just lay in her Moses basket, staring at her own hands.

'She looks very pleased,' one of them said, but we all knew he was just making it up.

9th June

Uncle Harry was in the newspapers this morning because he went to that Albert Hall we own for a charity concert last night. Mummy and Daddy talked about it over breakfast.

'Who was playing?' Daddy asked.

'Tony Bennett and Gaga,' Mummy said.

Daddy looked up from his boiled egg. 'Was she?' he asked, looking surprised. 'I didn't know she could sing?'

Mummy put down her superfood smoothie.

' "*Didn't know she could sing*"? Are you joking? She has sold twenty-eight million albums and won six Grammys. The woman can play the piano with her feet.'

'Really?' Daddy shook his head. 'I had no idea.'

'She is the shepherd of the dispossessed. The outcasts' champion,' Mummy went on. 'And she's not a one-trick pony, she has range – last night was a jazz concert.'

'I didn't even know she was fond of jazz,' Daddy said, baffled.

'Spike said she was wearing massive stuck-on

diamanté eyebrows,' Mummy said. 'Apparently he's now a converted monster.'

'A what?'

'You know, a monster,' Mummy said. 'It's what her fans call her. She is Mother Monster.'

'How can I not have known any of this about her?' Daddy asked.

'I have no idea,' Mummy said. 'I would have thought it was impossible not to.'

'Was Pa there?' Daddy asked.

'No, I don't think so. Not really his sort of thing.'

'That must be hard for her,' Daddy said.

'Why?'

'Well, it's not very supportive.'

Mummy frowned. 'I don't think she minds,' she said. 'She has something like fifty million followers on Twitter – that's quite a lot of support.'

'I didn't even know she was on Twitter,' Daddy said. 'I'm learning a lot this morning.'

'Well, of course she is,' Mummy said. She shook her head. 'Who goes around not knowing anything about Lady Gaga?'

Daddy put down his knife. 'No, Babykins,' he said gently. 'You're only a "lady" when you're the daughter of a duke, marquess or earl, or if you marry a peer or a knight. GaGa is a duchess. The Duchess of Cornwall. You know that.'

Mummy stared at Daddy from across the table. 'I'm

talking about Lady Gaga THE SINGER,' she said. 'Wearer of a meat dress, singer of a song called "Bad Romance", owner of a dog called Asia.'

Daddy went very pink. 'Ah,' he said.

'Not GaGa your stepmother,' Mummy said. 'Thanks for the *Debrett's* refresher course, though.'

Daddy went even pinker. 'They're easily confused,' he said, in a tiny voice.

'Of course they are,' Mummy said. 'What with one of them being an American superstar who sometimes carries a plastic arm around for no reason and the other coming from East Sussex and being married to your father.'

'This is so embarrassing,' Daddy said.

Mummy looked at him and smiled. 'How I enjoy you.'

'Maybe don't mention it to Spike.'

But Mummy was already texting on her phone. 'Oops,' she said, pressing send.

10th June

Happy birthday, G-Pop!!!! He is TEN MILLION years old today!!!! Uncle Harry told me that.

We didn't get to see him because we are at Anmer, but Daddy rang him when he got back from work, putting on loudspeaker so we could all hear him.

'Happy birthday!' Mummy and Daddy said, when he came onto the line.

'Yes,' G-Pop said.

'How has your day been?' Daddy asked.

'Have you ever had a birthday?' G-Pop also asked.

'Yes,' Daddy said.

'Well, it was like that,' G-Pop said crossly. 'Impertinent remarks about my age, presents from complete strangers that I have to generate some kind of gratitude for and ridiculously loud gun salutes. Damn fool question.'

'I see,' Daddy said.

'Is that it?' G-Pop asked. 'Because my left foot is starting to cramp and I want to get up.'

'G-Pop, you're on a portable phone,' Daddy said. 'You can get up now.'

'Bye,' G-Pop said, and the line went dead.

Mummy and Daddy looked at each other.

'I thought that went well,' Mummy said.

11th June

A big team meeting this morning. It is Trooping the Colour for GG's official birthday in two days' time, which ends with the whole fam at HQ for a balcony appearance. My team have been working on this wardrobe strategy for weeks and seemed very pleased with themselves when we sat down to discuss it.

'The keyword for this look,' my stylist said, 'is "heritage".'

'Yes,' my head of Global Strategy said. 'This ceremony dates back to the seventeenth century, so we want to create a strong nostalgia story for the press.'

'We've come up with something special,' my Media Manager said. 'A father-and-son narrative that will bring the world to its knees.'

My stylist produced a blue outfit. A romper of sorts. Vintage.

'The Duke of Cambridge wore this in 1984,' she said. 'He entranced the nation.'

'But it's time to go to the next level,' my Press Secretary said, 'and bewitch the world.'

'*Again*,' my Media Manager added.

Everyone applauded.

'We'll release the original photo of the Duke with the Prince of Wales to sit alongside the ones that will be captured of you with them both now,' my head of Global Strategy said.

Seemed like a plan. I've heard the eighties are coming back into fashion.

I am mostly excited about seeing the Red Arrows, who will fly over our heads and draw stripes in the sky. They are not actually arrows. They are planes that can fly in perfect formation or upside down without anyone falling out.

Bring it, Saturday!!

13th June

It was the big balcony day today. Yessssss.

I didn't go to the actual trooping bit because I was too busy getting ready, but we saw a lot of the action from a window at HQ.

Daddy's romper was a perfect fit. They pretended not to get teary, but it was perfectly obvious that some people are still very fond of the eighties and wish they could wear their clothes from back then too. The only person who couldn't have cared less was the unimpressable Lotto, who did not show any signs of being even remotely upset that she wasn't going to be part of the whole balcony showdown. Apart from when she is tired or hungry, her emotions remain unreadable.

Most of the family were in full military uniform. Daddy is Colonel of the Irish Guards and Goonie is Colonel of the Welsh – everyone's Colonel of something, but GG is the winner because she is Colonel-in-Chief of the lot of them.

We hung around a bit in the corridor behind the balcony window to get the crowd going before we appeared. The whole gang was there, so everyone had to make sure they'd curtsied to the right person. It was chaos, with constant cries of 'Sorry, have I done you yet?' and so forth.

'If I might have your attention, please?' GG then

said. 'Let's just talk about where we're all going to stand.'

There was immediate tension.

'I suggest Wales and Cambridge on my right,' she said. 'Wessex and York on my left.'

'What about Edinburgh?' G-Pop said crossly. 'I suppose he just lags behind in the shadows like a –'

'Ninja,' Uncle Harry said.

'What's that?' G-Pop said. 'A ginger? I should hope not. Ghastly creatures, gingers.'

Uncle Harry, Mummy and Daddy got terrible giggles.

'Thanks, Big Guy,' Uncle Harry said.

'Big who?' G-Pop said.

'Nothing – it's just, I'm obviously a ginger,' Uncle Harry said, as Mummy and Daddy's shoulders shook.

'I know, I know,' G-Pop said, shaking his head. 'Frightful bind.'

'I'm one too,' Cousin Bea piped up cheerfully. 'Loud and proud. Just like Mummy.'

G-Pop looked startled. 'Don't remind me,' he said, his eyes peering round the room. 'Not here, is she?'

Great Uncle Andy sighed loudly.

'Thought we'd managed to shake her off years ago,' G-Pop said.

Great Uncle Andy rolled his eyes. '*Really*, Mummy? Must I be expected to STILL put up with this?' he said to GG.

'We've gone past the point where it's worth the fight,' GG said. 'It simply wouldn't have any impact – like taking a deckchair off the *Titanic*.'

'Here's an idea,' Great Aunt Annie said. 'Let's thrash this out over a game of Chinese Chequers.'

GaGa pulled a face at us. 'I'm not sure there's time,' she said gently. 'Afterwards, perhaps?'

'Fine, but I'm going to start working out the teams now,' Great Aunt Annie said. 'You can be on mine, as long as you can guarantee you'll take it seriously. Can you talk me through any of the previous winning strategies you've used?'

'Yes: making sure the gin flows like a river!' GaGa and Goonie looked at each other and both roared with laughter.

'I could do with a gin now, I can tell you,' Great Uncle Andy muttered to himself. 'And I've been tee-total since I was nineteen.'

'Can we get a move on, please?' Great Uncle Eddie said. 'I've got a meeting after this.'

Great Uncle Andy laughed loudly. 'Er, no, you have not,' he said.

'Yes, I have, actually,' Great Uncle Eddie said. 'An important one.'

'OK – what's it about?' Great Uncle Andy said.

'It's about a show I've got in development, if you must know,' Great Uncle Eddie said testily. 'They need me for the important decisions.'

'Of course they do. Like who gets tea and who gets coffee,' Great Uncle Andy said. 'And shall we flip a coin for the last chocolate biscuit.'

Great Uncle Eddie lunged at him. 'Bastard!' he shouted. Great Uncle Andy made a break for it and Great Uncle Eddie raced after him.

GG shook her head. 'They've been like this since they were children. At each other's throats one minute, best of friends the next.'

'What sport – I adore this sort of thing. Shall we join in?' Goonie said, nudging Uncle Harry gently in the ribs.

'What a good idea,' Uncle Harry said. 'Come on, Wombat, let's show them how it's done.'

'I'm not sure that's a –' Daddy started to say, when Uncle Harry rushed at him and knocked him over. They wrestled on the floor.

'Ow! Careful of my medals!' Daddy shouted, as Uncle Harry went for the traditional headlock.

Great Aunt Annie sized up Goonie. 'What's the bet I could still take down Charles?' she said to Mummy.

'I'm not sure,' Mummy said. 'A fiver each way?'

She and Uncle Harry shot a glance at each other, even though he was in the middle of giving Daddy a dead leg.

The Mean Girls were THRILLED with all the fighting and got stuck in too, barking and taking swipes at everyone thrashing about on the floor, until Great

Uncle Eddie kicked one of them by mistake and that was the straw that broke GG's back.

'That's enough!' she said sternly, clapping her hands. 'What do you think this is? An episode of *EastEnders*?'

'How do you know about –' Great Uncle Andy said from the floor, where he had pinned Great Uncle Eddie's arm behind his back.

'You're not going to ask me how I know about *East-Enders*, are you?' GG said. 'Am I really expected to answer that? Very well – because I am the Queen. And I know everything there is to know about this country. And, anyway, that's not the point.' She turned to GaGa briefly and said under her breath, 'Don't tell me what happened with Masood and Shabnam yesterday because I haven't had time to watch it yet.'

GaGa pretended to zip her mouth, while GG turned back to address the brawlers. 'Might we dare to dream for the faintest hint of decorum?'

'Yes,' they said, getting up and hanging their heads.

'Good. Because otherwise I'm taking everyone's titles away and you can all go and buy your own houses.'

Great Aunt Soph gripped the edge of a table to steady herself.

'Fine by me,' Uncle Harry started saying, until Great Uncle Andy kicked him sharply in the shins.

'Sorry, Mummy,' Great Uncle Andy and Great Uncle Eddie said.

'Sorry, Granny,' Uncle Harry and Daddy said.

GG rolled her eyes. 'It's like herding cats,' she said, as the balcony doors were opened.

There was a big roar as we stepped out. So many people! I pointed at them to make sure no one missed it, because it was quite a sight. Daddy picked me up and we watched the planes fly overhead – the Red Arrows were THE DREAM. Noisy, stripy – everything you could possibly want. All this, but I never forgot there was a job to do. I waved constantly.

'At least there's one of you I don't have to worry about,' GG said. 'You're a pro, George.'

Great Uncle Andy and Uncle Harry jostled about, loitering in the background.

'Just so we're clear,' I heard Great Uncle Andy say, 'I totally won that fight.'

'Me too,' Uncle Harry said. 'But I always win. It's like fighting a cardigan.' He gave Daddy a slap on the bottom. 'Dear old Wombat. He's a lover, not a fighter.'

Great Uncle Eddie turned to Great Uncle Andy from the other side of the balcony and mouthed, 'I want a rematch,' but Great Uncle Andy just blew him a kiss.

I wonder if Lotto will want to fight me one day. I seriously hope not. Who knows what that secretive mind is capable of?

Anyway, after that we went in and had lunch, and GG said Great Uncle Andy and Great Uncle Eddie had to sit at separate ends of the table for 'behaving worse than the dogs'.

In spite of this, Great Uncle Eddie still managed to sneak a blini with caviar on it onto Great Uncle Andy's chair without him seeing. He's still walking round with it stuck to his trousers.

14th June

We had a debrief this morning to go over the press coverage from yesterday. The team were, as usual, frightfully pleased.

' "Prince George steals the show," ' my Press Secretary read aloud from a newspaper.

'They loved the heritage-wardrobe story,' my stylist said.

'And they loved the waving,' my Mood Analyst said.

'The world adores,' my head of Global Strategy said.

Everyone cheered.

We celebrated by going to see Daddy play in a polo match. I tried to persuade Lotto at least to give polo a chance, but she wasn't having any of it. She would rather sit in her bouncy chair and play with her textured octopus with the crunchy-sounding legs. There's no pleasing some people.

Polo is good, yes, but so is rolling down a grassy bank, getting covered with grass, picking up handfuls of grass, throwing grass and running off whenever the opportunity presents itself. Mummy also brought my mallet and ball so I could have a quick practice in case either of the teams needed a substitute, but they seemed to manage without me, and Uncle Harry's side ended up winning.

'FYI, I let you win,' Daddy said afterwards.

Uncle Harry sighed. 'Of course you did, darling. And I am secretly a unicorn.'

'Ladies,' Mummy said. 'Do let's get off the train to Yawnsville.'

I'm pretty tired now. But I can't believe I didn't know that Uncle Harry is secretly a unicorn.

15th June

Daddy was so excited this morning. 'I knew it. I KNEW IT,' he kept saying. 'It wasn't all in my mind.'

'That sounds ominous,' Mummy said. 'What are you talking about?'

'Oh, nothing – just going to a thing to celebrate Magna Carta today,' Daddy said, doing a strange move that made him look like he was brushing something off his shoulders. He then sang something about a holy grail and started rapping. 'Definitely Jay's greatest album in my opinion.'

The faintest hint of a smile appeared on Mummy's face, but she said nothing.

'It might not come up,' Daddy said, making a diamond shape with his hands, 'but if it does, I could ask him about being Lotto's godfather.'

'Please do,' Mummy said. 'And tell Bey I said hi.'

'I will,' Daddy said. 'Maybe I'll ask them for dinner.'

'What a good idea,' Mummy said. 'Can't wait to hear all about it.'

When Daddy came back at the end of the day, he looked a bit sheepish.

'How was Jay?' Mummy asked brightly. 'And how was Bey? Did you sit next to Justin Timberlake? Did Kanye give you some of his leather jogging pants?'

'Ummm . . .' Daddy said.

'Hope they can make it to the christening,' Mummy went on. 'Did you ask him about it?'

'Err . . .' Daddy said, going a bit pink.

'What?' Mummy said, making an innocent face.

'Yup, so it turns out it wasn't *Magna Carta* the Jay Z album after all,' Daddy said quietly. 'It was the other one.'

'Wait. What? No Jay Z? No Bey? No sitting next to Justin Timberlake? No swapping parenting stories with Kanye?' Mummy said.

'No. Just GG and G-Pop and Great Aunt Annie and David,' Daddy said. 'In Runnymede.'

'But that's so weird,' Mummy said. 'Because that would mean it WAS all in your mind.'

Daddy went even pinker. 'Not that it wasn't memorable in its own way,' he said.

Mummy patted him on the back. 'Thank you for being the most entertaining person I know.'

'Oh, bloody hell,' Daddy said.

And then Mummy started singing something about a concrete jungle and Daddy cheered up and joined in and even Lupo had to leave the room.

16th June

Mummy, Daddy and Uncle Harry are in total trauma this morning. Apparently the current series of that show *Game of Thrones* ended last night and someone they love appears to have ended up surprisingly dead.

'It can't be true,' Uncle Harry kept saying.

'It *cannot* be true,' Mummy said too.

'You two could be making it up for all I know,' Daddy said.

'We could never have come up with that,' Mummy said. 'Not even for a joke.'

'You could always actually just watch it with your own eyes instead of hiding and asking us to describe what's happening,' Uncle Harry said, 'and then you'd know.'

Daddy shuddered. 'I don't think so,' he said. 'Last night proved that.'

'How are we supposed to concentrate on ANY-THING today?' Uncle Harry asked. 'I've got to go to Ascot and then meet Michelle Obama for tea. I'll be there in body alone.'

Mummy gripped his arm. 'You have to ask her if he's actually dead – or only very seriously wounded indeed,' she said.

'She's not going to know, is she?' Uncle Harry said.

'She's the First Lady of the United States of America,' Daddy said. 'She can find out.'

'Or we could tell David to ring Barack,' Mummy said. 'Let's get the government involved. Someone somewhere must know *something*.'

At the end of the day Uncle Harry came and had supper with us and said Ascot was nothing but a total blur seen through traumatized eyes, and that he'd asked Michelle Obama about the person getting killed in *Game of Thrones* but she'd said she didn't know.

'That's it, I'm ringing Barack,' Daddy said. He picked up the phone. 'Hello. May I have a secure line, please? I need to speak to the President of the United States.'

There was a bit of a wait.

'Mr President? It's William,' Daddy said. ''S up?'

Mummy's eyes widened. Uncle Harry smacked his hand to his head. *'No. You. Didn't,'* he whispered.

'Just a quick question because I know you're busy. *Game of Thrones* – is he actually dead?'

There was talking at the other end. Daddy nodded.

'Yes ... Yes ... I see,' he said seriously. 'Thanks awfully ... OK ... Yup. Word.'

'*Word?*' Mummy mouthed in disbelief.

'Bye, thanks so much, bye,' Daddy said. He put the phone down.

'We'll mock you ruthlessly for the ill-judged slang later,' Uncle Harry said, 'but first – what does he know?'

'He says he thinks he's really gone,' Daddy said gravely. 'Actually dead.'

No one said a word for the rest of the evening. It's the first time Uncle Harry has been silent in thirty years.

18th June

Today is the 200th anniversary of the Battle of Waterloo, so Goonie, GaGa, Great Uncle Eddie and David went to St Paul's to celebrate how brilliant that was. What happened is that the Duke of Wellington beat Napoleon Bonaparte in an enormous fight and that's why we have wellington boots because he gave Bonaparte the boot out of Belgium. Uncle Harry told me that.

19th June

Uncle Harry's career in the army officially ends today! He didn't apply to be our new housekeeper, like

Mummy suggested, and now someone else has taken that job. 'You snooze, you lose,' as GaGa would say.

20th June

Tomorrow is Daddy's birthday. Not only that, it is also Father's Day. I am SO EXCITED. Mummy spent the afternoon wrapping presents for him and I helped. Which means I only hid the Sellotape once and stopped ripping the paper when Mummy asked me to.

I made Daddy a picture in my art class – it is of him flying his helicopter. He is represented by a green hand-print and the helicopter is the bit of yellow paint I knocked over on the paper by mistake. I hope he likes it!

Lotto prepared nothing, of course, so Mummy decided to intervene to save her from disgrace tomorrow. She dipped Lotto's feet in some paint and then pressed them onto a mug. Lotto wasn't very happy about it and made her cat-alien noise, which was odd because it looked like a lot of fun to me. I dipped my hands in the paint and pressed them onto Lotto's dress to show her. Then it was Mummy's turn to be not very happy.

21st June

Happy birthday, Daddy! He is THIRTY-THREE years old!!! That is one Uncle Harry and one and a half Georges put together!!!!

You also get a present today if you are a father because they also made it Father's Day. Daddy was extremely happy with my picture, I'm pleased to say. He says he's going to keep it in his helicopter. He also loved Lotto's foot mug and kept kissing her actual feet, like he was her slave and she was queen of the universe. She tolerated it, but nothing more. You know what she's like.

Mummy and Daddy are having dinner at home tonight. They're both wearing animal onesies and Mummy has arranged a special screening of a classic film called *Finding Nemo* – although they have to fast-forward the beginning because Daddy gets upset when Nemo's mother dies.

23rd June

I was at HQ today for GG and David's weekly meeting when David coughed and a chunk of the cornicing fell down. 'Golly,' he said, blushing deeply. 'Was that me?'

'No,' GG said, looking up at the ceiling. 'It's just that

it's been a while since we redecorated. I do apologize if it gave you a shock.'

'Oh, no, please don't worry,' David said. 'It wasn't worse than the shock I got when George told me what he weighs this week.'

'I see,' GG said. 'The 5:2 continues to deliver?'

'Yes, but how much longer can he keep it up for?' David said. 'If this were a competition – and I'm not saying it is – then I would be the tortoise and he would be the hare. He's going for quick results, but I'm being much more tactical than him.'

'Are you still running?' GG asked.

'Only because I have to,' David said dejectedly. 'Can you imagine what the press would say if I gave up? "Cameron can't run the country, let alone around the block." '

'That's rather good,' GG said.

'It's a bit demoralizing, if I'm honest, because it seems to be having the reverse effect,' he said. 'All this effort and I put on two pounds this week.'

GG cut herself a piece of cake.

'No, no – that's too much for me,' David said. 'I could only manage half.'

'Oh,' GG said. 'I thought you were wheat-free?'

'I am, I am,' David said. 'I just need a pick-me-up today.'

GG handed him the plate and he cut the piece of cake into two. And then he ate both halves. 'Don't tell anyone,' he said, sighing, 'but I had half a packet of Digestives in the car on the way here. It's just a blip, though.'

'I'm sure,' GG said.

'George says he doesn't have blips, but I saw him looking at the croissants in this morning's cabinet meeting. He was wavering, I know he was wavering.'

'Indeed,' GG said calmly. 'And now, Prime Minister – let us return to the matter in hand.'

'Oh!' David said, putting down the sandwich he had in his hand. 'I don't even remember picking that up.'

'I meant the Greek debt crisis.'

'Absolutely,' David said, taking a bite out of the sandwich he had in his other hand.

24th June

GG and G-Pop may have to move out of HQ while they rebuild the bits that keep falling off. They might even fix the heating during the renovations, which no one has bothered with for years because G-Pop doesn't really believe in central heating.

'We only had a single generator run by a goat on a treadmill in Mon Repos, when I was a child, and we managed perfectly well,' he always says.

26th June

Today we saw those people again for tea at our house – Brad and Angelina. The ones who look like they were made by NASA. Even Lotto went into total visual lockdown on them when they came into the room. It's the most transfixed I've ever seen her.

They talked about the preservation of endangered animals for a lot of the conversation. And then they talked about . . . well, I think it was babies.

'I just always found birth such a leonine experience,' Angelina said. 'Like I revealed my primitive self and connected with the universe, you know?'

'Err . . .' Mummy said.

'Each contraction was like a conversation between the earth's core and my core,' Angelina went on. 'I mean, it's like I was every woman who has given birth in that moment. I felt that infinite understanding, that knowledge, that passion for humanity.'

'Wow . . .' Daddy said, nodding seriously.

'And while we weren't there for the physical births of our other kids, we are so blessed to have been there to nurture their spiritual births,' Brad said, taking Angelina's hand. 'Parenthood continues to be such a nourishing, vivifying experience. I mean, they teach *us*. Every day, we're, like, "Whoa, your higher self is really educating me right now." '

Mummy and Daddy looked at Lotto and me. Lotto had sicked up over the cashmere cardigan Brad and Angelina had given her as a present and I was trying to fit Mummy's iPhone into my mouth.

'Where do you keep your Oscar?' Mummy asked Angelina, as she wiped under Lotto's chin and put her iPhone out of my reach.

'We had it melted down and turned into a plaque to commemorate the fifty-nine point five million people currently displaced by war,' Angelina said.

'Gosh,' Mummy said.

'Don't suppose you know the inside story on what happened in the final episode of *Game of Thrones*, do you?' Daddy asked. 'Catherine and I are still in shock.'

Brad and Angelina looked at each other.

'*Game of Thrones?*' Brad said.

'What's that?' Angelina said.

'Don't you watch it?' Mummy asked, trying not to sound horrified but totally failing.

Angelina blinked her big, beautiful, whirlpool eyes. 'Is it a TV show?'

'We don't have a television,' Brad explained, the sunlight bouncing off his perfect skin. 'We prefer to read aloud with the kids or expatiate verbally on a broad range of edifying topics.'

'Globalization, gender fluidity, racial otherness . . .' Angelina added.

'How wonderful,' Daddy said. 'I am absolutely fascinated by gender fluid.'

After they'd gone, Mummy and Daddy couldn't stop talking about them.

'It's like looking directly at the sun,' Mummy was saying. 'You sort of almost have to avert your gaze because, if you look at them for too long, you could go blind.'

'I'm worried about G's classes now,' Daddy said, looking at me. 'I thought we were doing all right, but perhaps he ought to be studying racial globalization and gender otherness.'

'I agree,' Mummy said, 'but let's wait until he's three.'

28th June

Mummy and Daddy have become completely fixated with the Women's World Cup. Our team, the Lionesses, is now in the actual quarter-finals. Mummy keeps hiding round the house, then suddenly jumping out on Daddy and shouting, 'Raaaaaaah!!!!' like a lioness and he leaps out of his skin, screaming, every time.

They've been staying up late to watch their matches and yesterday we all painted our faces like lions to show our support.

July 2015

1st July

Happy Canada Day!

We are having maple syrup with everything today to celebrate. Mummy even had some on her salad and Daddy had some in the chicken sandwich he took to work.

Daddy called the Lionesses today to tell them himself that they are doing a brilliant job because he is President of the Football Association. He roared down the phone when they answered and nobody understood it was him, so he had to say, 'Er, sorry – it's William. The, er, the Duke of Cambridge.'

And then they were excited.

Mummy was laughing so much she had to leave the room – but not before she'd jumped on Daddy's back, growling so loudly he had to pretend there was a problem with the line.

And when he was off the phone, Daddy went and got Lotto and held her up above his head in both hands and started to sing 'Circle Of Life' from *The Lion King* and Mummy laughed and then looked like she might cry but I think it was more like the happy crying she told me about in Mustique.

3rd July

The Lionesses got beaten last night and are out of the World Cup. Total sorrow. Daddy has stopped talking and has just painted his own face like a lion in their honour. There are flesh lines down the middle where his tears have washed the paint away.

We are at Anmer again because Lotto has her christening on Sunday and we have A LOT to organize. It's very lucky, actually, because at least it helps distract from the footballing trauma.

My team have been hard at it as usual, working on my look and strategy for this event. Lotto will be lolling about in a pram, so Mummy, Daddy and I are shouldering most of the attention.

Lotto has to wear that enormous dress I wore at my christening, which is a replica of the one Great Great Great Great Great Grandmother Victoria wore to her christening. It's so long – I mean, you couldn't play football in it or anything. I may have to break this to Lotto – in case she was planning some kind of vigorous physical activity for that day, LOL.

On to more important things. My outfit.

We had a meeting to discuss where the team had got to with their plans for my own christening look. I sat in my high chair and played with my animal noises book (lest we forget the whole 'It's a tiger!' debacle when I did my bear noise – someone needs to educate these people).

They were looking at different outfits on a rail and discussing the options.

'We've done blue and we've done white, both to great acclaim,' my head of Global Strategy was saying. 'Are we thinking we should stick to this winning formula?'

'Yes, very much so,' my stylist said. 'It's what the people want.'

No, no, no.

Clearly this was a day for tradition, for nostalgia and low-level sentimentality. It was obvious if Lotto was going to be wearing a replica family outfit, I should be too.

I threw my book down.

'Wait!' my Press Secretary said. 'Prince George wants to tell us something.'

I banged the table. Shouted a bit. Pointed at my colouring pens.

'Quick!' someone cried. 'The pens!'

'He wants to give us a colour scheme,' my Mood Analyst said. 'We need paper immediately!'

There was a terrific scuffle. Someone produced a pad and the pens were put in front of me.

It was time to switch things up a bit – so I reached for the red at once and drew firmly across the page. And a bit on my hands. And nose.

'Red! Brilliant, brilliant,' my stylist said. 'Of course!'

I then drew some squiggly lines.

'What do you think this means?' my Hairdresser asked. 'Is it . . . trousers of some sort?'

Trousers. In July. I ask you.

I directed the pen at my own top and squiggled again.

'Embroidery!' someone shouted. 'He's right! He's totally right!'

A cry of 'Get him out of that chair!' went up.

I ran towards a framed photo of Daddy on the mantlepiece and pointed at it.

'Wait – I've got it!' my stylist said, turning to her 'Royal Looks through the Decades' folder. 'This look from 1984 – the young Duke visits the newborn Prince Harry in a white top with red embroidery and red shorts. It's the heritage theme again!'

'Of course – it was a global smash last time,' my Media Manager said. 'The whole day is about heritage.' He turned to me. 'Invaluable input, as usual, Sir,' he said. 'Rest assured, we're on it.'

Well.

They got there in the end.

5th July

Lotto's christening, so a big day. Mummy and Daddy didn't go for anyone from One Direction or Ran-Ran the elephant as godparents in the end, just friends and family. Probably not a bad idea as the crowds were already enormous outside the church without any 1D fans and, to be honest, there is no way Ran-Ran would have got through the church door.

Mummy pushed Lotto in her pram and I walked with Daddy in front of the world's press. I wanted to stop and thank the police and chat to the crowd, but there wasn't time. I had to check on GG to see if she was OK, check on Lotto to see if she was OK (she was just lying there staring at the sky without a care in the world, as we have come to expect of her) and check to see if the rest of the family were coping with the scrutiny. There were so many people to take into consideration – even the Arch needed a reassuring tug of his dress from me to make sure he was feeling prepared.

Inside the church, there was a bit of singing and a bit of reading, then the Arch poured water on Lotto's head and it was all quite boring.

After tea we had a photo session with Mario. Mario is a very good photographer – you could have apple juice down your top and cake in your hair and STILL he would make you look good.

Then Uncle Harry tapped the side of his champagne glass and said Lotto wanted to make a speech. He picked her up in her long dress and rocked her a bit in one arm. 'Lotto has asked me to thank you for all coming here today to celebrate her rejection of Satan while wearing a stupid dress.'

Everyone clapped. Lotto continued to stare disinterestedly at the sky.

'She is grateful for the wonderful party and all the lovely presents you have given her. She wishes she could say it has been a memorable day, but of course, she can't – because she won't remember any of it. Not even the part where the Archbishop of Canterbury flicked water in her face and George tried to look up his dress. And yet in spite of this, she would still like to say a few words.'

He turned to Daddy. 'To Daddy – thank you for laughing that time I peed all over your shirt and for always singing to me. It goes some way to make up for the rapping. Not a long way, but it helps.'

Then he turned to Mummy. 'To Mummy – thank you for all my milk, for telling me I'm pretty four hundred times a day and for passing on the great gift of projectile vomiting. I know I learnt from the best.'

Mummy and Daddy put their arms around each other.

Then to me. 'To my brother, George – I am learning so much from you about shouting, throwing things and slamming doors. The way you splash in the bath is truly inspirational. Thank you for being an excellent brother. I can't wait to draw on GG's Tintorettos with you.'

Yikes, how did they know about that?

GG was next. 'To my great-grandmother, GG – you are the greatest monarch this country has ever seen and still you continue to smash it in your pastels and mid-height heels. Please teach me the gift of small talk and how to not look disappointed when someone gives me flowers they clearly bought at a garage.

'It's not easy, I can tell you,' GG said.

Then it was G-Pop. 'To my great-grandfather, G-Pop – you are GG's rock. Your gentle, sweet manner and natural diplomacy are a lesson to us all in how to build international relations with prudence and sensitivity.'

'I'm glad someone noticed,' G-Pop said crossly.

'To Goonie and GaGa – if I am persuaded to give up fags in favour of drinking dandelion juice and bee sweat, I too will know that I have found true love.'

Goonie and GaGa roared with laughter and hugged each other.

'To Granny C, Grandpa M and Uncle J – thank you for helping me keep my feet on the ground. I look forward to learning, not only how to make sure my sponges come out evenly, but also the basics of what to do in the unlikely event of an emergency landing.'

They all cheered.

'To the Arch – nice dress.'

The Arch waved at Lotto.

'To my godparents – remember – you will be judged for your presents. Falling short of my standards will end only one way: permanent imprisonment in the Tower. With no trial.'

All the godparents laughed – but slightly nervously.

'And to my Uncle Harry – not only are you astonishingly handsome, you are an outstanding dancer, uncle and human being. As my greatest influence and fellow "spare", I look forward to plotting how to bring down my older sibling and claiming the throne for myself.'

Everything had been going fine until he said that – but I looked at Lotto, who had fallen asleep and realised that if you're going to be the sort of person who stages a coup, you probably need to be awake for it.

'Last but not least – to my Aunt P. One day I will be second in line to the throne, so I could actually command this like we did in the good old days – however, as a modern princess, I will instead say it is my dearest wish that you should marry my Uncle Harry. As the world's most enduring optimist, he's going to put aside the personal humiliation of the last two occasions on which you turned him down and hope that a third offer will be the lucky one.'

'Three is the magic number,' Aunt P said.

'Lotto feels strongly, as does the whole of the human race, that Uncle Harry would make an excellent husband for you. His many skills have been documented and he is prepared to get you a ring that not only fits, but is also not neon plastic. As for this random guy you're seeing – Lotto agrees that he's perfectly nice if you like that sort of thing – but can he claim to have ever been nicknamed 'the bullet magnet' while serving his country in Afghanistan and can he break dance?'

'You can't break dance,' Mummy said. 'You ripped your trousers the last time you tried.'

'True,' Uncle Harry said. 'But I would wander the world in ripped trousers if it would win me P's hand in marriage. The Arch is feet away from us – we could close the deal right now? What do you say, my beloved?'

Aunt P pursed her lips. Everyone waited.

'I need to think about it,' she said. Uncle Harry held his breath. 'Give me twenty years.'

'Well, that's fine,' Uncle Harry said, 'because I will wait for you. I might seek comfort in the arms of numberless others, FYI, but I will always compare them unfavourably to you.'

'Nice,' Aunt P said. 'It's what every girl wants to hear.'

'I know,' Uncle Harry said. 'I'm VERY good at this stuff.'

Uncle Harry is a deeply romantic person. I hope he keeps asking Aunt P because one day she will have to say yes, even if it's just to shut him up.

8th July

We are back in London again. This was so Mummy and Daddy could go and watch the tennis at Wimbledon. They went to cheer for Andy Murray, who Uncle Harry said used to be Scottish until he won and now he's British. I wonder if that means he plays wearing one of those skirts?

Anyway, they were in a very good mood when they got home.

'Romeo Beckham is such a looker,' Mummy said. 'I wish I'd asked him for a selfie. As for David, that man is like a fine wine – he just gets better and better with age.'

'Did you see how much they laughed at my joke?' Daddy kept saying. 'Literally the whole of Centre Court.'

'It was a good gag,' Mummy said.

'Me pretending to run for the tube when that tube strike announcement came over the Tannoy . . .' Daddy said, laughing to himself. 'They loved it.'

'The only thing is,' Mummy said, 'do you actually know what the tube is?'

'Well, no,' Daddy said seriously. 'Is it some sort of slide?'

I went to play with GG and David while Mummy and Daddy were busy because today is one of the last days I will see David before the summer holidays.

He turned up wearing a pair of very strange shoes. And in a spectacularly cheerful mood.

'They're called "FitFlops",' he told GG. 'They tone different muscle groups when you walk in them – thighs, calves, glutes. Isn't that clever?'

'Yes, very,' GG said.

'I've been wearing them around Downing Street for the past week and I'm sure I can already feel a difference.'

'That's remarkable,' GG said.

'I don't know why I'm telling you all this, because it's probably obvious,' David said, admiring his own calves.

'Err . . .' GG said.

'They're definitely slimmer, aren't they?' David said.

'Yes,' GG said politely.

'And not just slimmer – this is the thing – stronger too,' David said. 'Just from simple old walking around. Imagine that!'

I decided to test this. So I ran up to David and kicked one of his allegedly iron calves.

'Didn't feel a thing,' he squeaked, his eyes watering as he rubbed the back of his leg.

'Then the shoes must be working,' GG said. 'And don't kick the Prime Minister, please, George.'

'Not the first time I've heard that sentence, I can tell you,' David said.

I went back to playing with the stone in GG's handbag.

'Anyway, the other George is so jealous,' he went on gleefully. 'He knows he can't get a pair too because it'll just look like copying.' He rubbed his hands together. 'I rather think this means I can eat what I want now,' he said, piling several sandwiches up on his plate. 'Because I'll just walk it off and it'll be like it never happened. What a result.'

'Speaking of results,' GG said, 'I should be very interested to hear more about your government's tax credit plans for this year.'

'George has trimmed nine billion pounds off the thirty billion annual bill for tax credits,' David said. 'And I've trimmed two inches off my waistline! Who's the winner now?' And then he laughed very loudly and said he would bring GG some fudge back from his holiday.

'If he brings back the box unopened, I'll give you Canada,' GG said to me, when he left.

As he walked out of the door, I noticed David's bottom looked slightly bigger than it had the last time we'd met.

9th July

The Lionesses came for breakfast with us today!

Mummy caught Daddy in the bathroom painting on his lion face, but she made him wash it off.

'Come on – let me do George and Lotto at least,' he said.

'The thing about the word "no" is that there's no room for misinterpretation,' Mummy said. 'It's not a word with nuance. It's just good old no.'

I thought we would give the Lionesses raw meat for breakfast, but we didn't. We gave them kedgeree, sausages and scrambled eggs, and Daddy did a photo with them. Raaaaaaaah!

They've given Lotto a football shirt. We showed it to her and she sort of waved a hand at it, which is more than we could have hoped for in terms of her expressing enthusiasm, so perhaps she has plans to join the team after all.

Then Uncle Harry came in wearing a controversial T-shirt that said, 'Football is never coming home'. Though it has to be said, he's so good with girls that they ended up loving him, especially when he explained that, because he's going to come second for the whole of his life, it's only fair to rib anyone who comes third.

Mario's christening photos got released to the press today as well. You could say they've gone down well #UnderstatementOfTheCentury.

!!!!!!!!!!!!

'Look at everyone in their pastels,' Mummy said, admiring the group family photo. 'We look like a plate of expensive macaroons. Mario is a *genius*.'

'J's beard is getting so intense,' Daddy said. 'And George is actually sitting still for once in his entire life.'

'Our children look like angels,' Mummy said. 'Georgie, you're so clever to have gone for the red embroidery.'

'YOU look like an angel, Babykins,' Daddy said, gazing dreamily at Mummy.

'And you look very handsome,' Mummy said. 'Well done us.'

10th July

Daddy went to HQ today for an RAF flypast to mark the seventy-fifth anniversary of the Battle of Britain. The Battle of Britain was a battle that happened in Britain, but in the sky. Luckily we won it and winning things always deserves a party, even if the thing you won was a long time ago.

Anyway, Daddy watched the old warplanes from the balcony with GG, G-Pop, Great Uncle Andy, Great Uncle Eddie and Great Aunt Soph.

Something hairy obviously happened afterwards, because Mummy's Press Secretary came in at one point and showed her a video I couldn't hear on his laptop and Mummy covered her mouth with her hand and they both gasped.

'Omfg,' Mummy said.

'Literally,' her Press Secretary said.

As soon as Daddy was home, Mummy asked him about the mystery incident.

Daddy put his face into his hands.

'So there we are, getting organized for the group photo and G-Pop just loses his rag and says to this photographer –' He stopped and looked at me, then looked back at Mummy. ' "Just take the *ducking* picture." '

Mummy glanced at me and then looked at Daddy. 'For duck's sake,' she said.

'He's a ducking liability,' Daddy said. 'I had to summon everything I have not to have total hysterics. I thought my face was going to fall off.'

'What a ducking nightmare,' Mummy said.

'I know. I mean, what the duck was he thinking?' Daddy said.

'He doesn't give a dying duck, that's what,' Mummy said.

Then they fell about laughing.

I don't know what all the fuss is about. G-Pop loves birds, everyone knows that. It's not a ducking secret.

13th July

We are back at Anmer because Daddy starts work as an ACTUAL air-ambulance pilot today. He will be known as Captain William Wales, not Willy the Flying

Wombat after all, so Uncle Harry was wrong. He is excited about his job and we are super-proud of him – this in spite of him saying ON CAMERA in an interview about it that Lotto is a 'little joy of heaven' and I am 'a little monkey'.

Not. Amused.

Again, I tried to draw Lotto on the subject. She eyed me stonily, then swiped at her lions-and-unicorns mobile. She has clearly become emboldened since she had water from the River Jordan poured on her head last week by the Arch. I didn't realize the idea was it adopted you into the Church AND gave you attitude.

Mummy keeps playing something called 'Ride of the Valkyries' and saying, 'I love the smell of Morston Marsh in the morning,' but I don't know what that means.

15th July

We are staying at Windsor for a couple of days while Daddy gets settled into his new job. G-Pop has been roaring around the grounds in his carriage, and GG has been visiting her stables at Polhampton.

'I've got my eye on the King George VI and Queen Elizabeth Diamond Stakes and I don't mind saying so,' GG told me, as she checked out the competition in the *Racing Post*. 'Who do you think has form?' she said, showing me the horses listed as entering.

I waved my pen at the page, drawing a line next to one of them.

GG studied the result.

'Very interesting,' she said, putting on her glasses. 'One of John Gosden's horses. He likes fast ground, which is good for this time of year, but he needs to be kept covered – likes to run with the pack. Might well be worth a nod each way – or even on the nose.'

Then we heard Mummy coming into the room.

'Let's keep this to ourselves,' GG said, bundling the *Racing Post* behind a cushion. 'But if your horse comes in, we'll split the winnings down the middle.'

Mummy sat down and GG poured her some tea.

'I don't know if this is an inappropriate thing to say, but the footmen here are SO good-looking,' Mummy said, marvelling at one who had just left the room.

'I know,' GG said. 'You should have seen our friend Mr John admiring them the last time he was here. I had to take him aside and say, "Don't get any ideas, Elton – we count them out and we count them in."'

17th July

Today is GaGa's birthday! She is SIXTY-EIGHT years old! That is more than two whole Mummys!!!!

Goonie and GaGa came for a birthday lunch with us, which GG managed to squeeze in between handing out some knighthoods and MBEs. We gave GaGa lots of presents and a big cake shaped like a packet of something called Marlboro Reds.

GaGa was wearing two badges, one that said 'Old enough to know better' and another that said 'I like laughing, chillaxing and bees!'

'Spike sent them to me.' GaGa guffawed. 'I adore them. I want to wear them every day.'

'What are you doing later?' Mummy asked GaGa.

'Aha! We've got the perfect evening planned,' she said. 'Dinner outside in the garden, couple of bottles of rosé, might even sneak in a cheeky birthday fag if this one doesn't object.' She nudged Goonie in the ribs.

'This one wouldn't dream of denying the birthday girl anything,' Goonie said. 'And when dinner is over, we can play some Leonard Cohen records. Doesn't that sound like heaven?'

'Oh Lord,' GaGa said, rolling her eyes. 'Debbie Downer.'

'What does that mean?' Goonie asked.

'You know – major depressor.'

'Major who?'

'Oh, Fred,' GaGa said, shaking her head. 'There's no hope for you.'

'There's no hope for me!' Goonie agreed heartily.

And then they both roared with laughter.

'Major Depressor, you say?' G-Pop suddenly said. 'I think I served with him in Ceylon. Ghastly man.'

Afterwards we went on a tour round the castle, so GG could show us the refurbishments that have recently been carried out.

We stopped by a window in the Lower Ward and GG pointed past St George's Chapel. 'This was my mother's favourite view from the castle,' she said. 'Although I suspect that was before they built Slough.'

20th July

Mummy and Daddy have been acting strangely all day.

'What's your favourite number?' Mummy keeps saying.

'Two – what's yours?' Daddy says back.

'Hey, mine's also two!' Mummy says.

And then they both look at me and smile.

What?

You'd think they could count higher than two. I mean, even I can get up to twenty.

21 July

'How does it feel?' Mummy said to me this morning.

I looked at her blankly.

'To be one for one last day?'

What?

'I can't believe it's your birthday tomorrow,' she said, sighing. 'My grown-up boy.'

I was so surprised that I tipped over Lupo's water bowl and then sat in the puddle.

'OK, maybe not so grown-up,' Mummy said, putting a new bib on Lotto that said, 'These fools put my cape on backwards.'

So THAT'S what it's all about – it's my birthday tomorrow! This is MEGA news. To celebrate, we released another photo of Daddy and me to the press today from our shoot with Mario. It's one of Mummy's favourites. In fact, it's the one I picked out for her when we were looking at the contact sheets.

'Prince George's instincts are spot-on once again,' my Media Manager said later on, in the afternoon. 'We've been trending on Twitter all day. You can't teach this kind of thing. Some people just have it.'

Lotto is showing zero interest in my birthday. She only cares about the textured octopus with the crunchy legs. I've run out of ideas with this baby. No one can say I haven't tried. We are clearly just very different people. Not all siblings end up being thick as thieves. Daddy and Uncle Harry were just a one-off. Apart from Mummy, Aunt P and Uncle J. Or GG and Great Great Aunt Margs. Or Great Uncle Andy and Great Uncle Eddie.

Oh, I give up.

22nd July

HAPPY BIRTHDAY TO ME!!!!! I am TWO. WHOLE. YEARS. OLD. That's almost eight Lottos!!!

My choir woke me by singing that birthday song and this time I knew how it went, so I joined in. Mummy, Daddy and Lotto were all wearing party hats that said 'George (is the) Best!' They gave one to me too. I'm never going to take it off.

'Two years old, Georgie,' Mummy said, carrying me to breakfast. 'You're ancient. How did this happen?'

'It feels like you were the size of a peanut only yesterday,' Daddy agreed. 'And now look at you – running around, slamming doors, constantly trying to shove a lemon into the DVD player.' He gave me a big kiss and tickled me under my arms.

'Today is all about you,' Mummy said. 'We're just going to play games and have fun because that is birthday law.'

So we did indeed spend the whole morning playing games. After I opened my presents, Mummy pretended to be a monster and chased Daddy, Lotto and me around the garden. Then we went on the swings and then we did some painting – I did a picture of a crocodile jumping out of a birthday cake but when I showed it to Mummy, she said, 'Oh look, it's a . . . canoe on top of a mountain?'

She handed it to Daddy.

'Or a fireman having a swim?' Daddy said.

Arrrgh!!

But it didn't really matter because we just ended up throwing paint at each other and laughing and it was SO BRILLIANT.

I'm not sure Lotto would have agreed, though. She didn't really join in unless Mummy or Daddy was carrying her. Otherwise she just sat in her bouncy chair at the side and watched. I tried to include her by showing her my new toy boat but she just yawned and then she went to sleep.

Granny C, Grandpa M, Aunt P and Uncle J came for lunch and, as usual, Uncle Harry was late.

He came bursting through the door shouting, 'Give me a "HELL, YEAH" if you're two today!' Then he did a strange dance.

'I learnt this in Kiribati,' he said. 'It brings good luck – can you tell?'

He said hello to everyone, stopping at Aunt P. 'My angel,' he said. 'You look so clean and healthy and you smell like freshly laundered sheets. Just like I've always imagined the future mother of my children would.'

'It's still a no,' Aunt P said. 'For now.'

'I'll get you in the end, young lady,' Uncle Harry said. 'Failing that, can I have the number of that mate of yours from the party you were photographed at last week because she is ADORABLE.'

'No,' Aunt P said.

'Oh dear,' Uncle Harry said, patting her shoulder. 'I think someone's a little bit jealous. Very good sign indeed. Things are looking up.'

Then he went and sat on Daddy's lap. 'How's my favourite baldy?' he said, kissing Daddy's forehead, then getting him in the usual headlock.

'That's quite tight, actually . . .' Daddy said, coughing and starting to turn bright red.

Uncle Harry dropped Daddy and gave me a hug. He's teaching me a fist-bumping routine, a bit like the one he does with Mummy, so we practised that too.

'Happy birthday, Small G, you incredibly short gangsta,' he said. 'Let's have a look at your loot – get anything decent?'

I showed him my haul.

'The clothes are boring, obviously, but I like your new boat,' he said. 'We're definitely playing with that after lunch. No arguments.' He went and picked up Lotto. 'And what birthday gossip have you got for me, big mouth?' he asked her. 'Everyone knows you can't keep quiet about anything.'

Lotto just stared at him.

'Daddy told you he's incredibly jealous of me because everyone knows I'm the handsome one?' he said. 'I agree – that IS undignified.'

Later on, GG and G-Pop came for tea and I showed

them the painting I did this morning of a crocodile jumping out of a birthday cake.

'Isn't that marvellous?' GG said. 'You've rather a gift for painting, George – hasn't he, Philip?'

GG passed my picture to G-Pop, who turned it round and round, frowning at it.

'Can't make head or tail of this,' he said. 'What is it? Some idiotic Cubist monstrosity where they paint some fellow with his nose on the side of his head or whatever it is these madmen try to pass off as art?'

GG laughed. 'No, no, no,' she said. 'It's a crocodile jumping out of a birthday cake. Why don't you show it to Lotto?' GG asked me. 'She would love it.'

I begged to differ – in that I said, 'No,' and played with my new boat instead.

GG watched me for a bit and then she suggested we went for a walk in the garden. We sat down on a bench and then she got that stone out of her bag and passed it to me. 'I know you're rather fond of this stone – and maybe you've been wondering why I always have it in my handbag,' she said. I looked at it in my hand.

'My sister – your Great Great Aunt Margaret – gave it to me when I was six and she was two, the same age as you. I'd thought she was rather a bore up until then, always wanting Mummy and Papa's attention and being a tremendous show-off. But then on my sixth birthday, I found her playing in the garden and she handed me this stone and said, "For Lilibet." From that day onward, she was my greatest friend.'

I put the stone into my mouth.

GG took it out again. 'The thing is, one needs an ally in this job. And no one fits the bill better than a sibling. A trusted companion one can let off steam to when things get tricky. When one has been judged or misunderstood and can't defend oneself. Someone who knows what a privilege it is to have this life, but who understands the pressure. Someone who will always be on your side – in spite of their insistence on hosting racy parties in Mustique when one has begged them not to.'

I thought about Lotto. The unreadable blob in the bouncy chair.

'I know Lotto doesn't seem terribly interesting to you now, but give her time,' GG said. 'She's wonderful – and she's going to be even more wonderful. Just like you.' She patted my knee. 'My sister isn't here any more. But when I hold this stone in my hand, she's with me again, marching up and down the drive at Birkhall, singing at the top of her lungs.'

We looked across the lawn. Mummy was lying on the grass with her head in Aunt P's lap, watching attentively while Uncle J showed them his new apron.

'And, yes, I know some people called her "the house guest from Hell", and perhaps she was overly fond of protocol, but they didn't know her like I did. She was also the funniest, most loyal and loving sister one could hope for.'

We heard Daddy yelp as Uncle Harry took a running jump at him and they both just fell over, howling with laughter.

'Completely outrageous too. One day I'll tell you about the night she got up and did the splits right in the middle of the table during dinner at the American Embassy. It caused the most frightful row at home,' she said. 'Gosh, I miss her.'

We walked back to the house hand in hand and I thought about what GG had said.

When we got there, I decided to go and find Lotto. She was lying in her bouncy chair, chewing one of her fists. The same expressionless face. I stood and looked at her. Might as well test out what GG was saying, I thought. So I jumped up in the air and roared like a lion.

And Lotto did something very weird. She smiled. A big, wet, gummy smile.

I did it again.

She smiled again and made a small 'gaaah' noise.

So I did it again.

And she did it again. But louder – 'GAAAH!'

'Lotto!' I said, and patted her on the head.

She gurgled and smiled. Again!

Mummy and Daddy watched from the doorway.

'She's smiling!' Daddy said.

'How could she not?' Mummy said. 'That's the best lion impression I've ever seen.'

'By the way,' Daddy said, 'GUESS WHO has been spotted in Dublin where they're filming the next series of *Game of Thrones*?'

'Omg,' Mummy said, gripping Daddy's arm. 'What? He might be alive after all?'

'I know. Could this day get any better?'

'Look, George turning two is good. And so is Lotto smiling for the first time. But that – THAT . . .' Mummy said.

I told you they watched too much TV.

Acknowledgements

This book has been a dream to write from start to finish, thanks to the enormous amount of encouragement I've had. Particular champions include Richard Curtis, Annabel Rivkin, Alexandra Heminsley, Margot Lyritzis, Maggie Castle and all the friends who have cheered me on. Sorry in advance that you're only going to get signed copies of this as birthday and Christmas presents for the next few years. Probably for ever.

Thanks to my family for the endless inspiration – Harry and William's constant fighting, Great Aunt Annie's violent games of RD, the mandatory nicknames and tribal loyalty to name a handful.

I owe an enormous debt of gratitude to Kate Reardon, Gavanndra Hodge and all my pals at *Tatler* for their support – it is a joy to write for the funniest magazine on the shelves. Long may it continue.

To my agent and old friend Simon Trewin – the only person who still consistently hangs up on me – I can't really verbalise how important you have been throughout this whole thing. I am so glad we overlooked that conversation where you once said I would make the worst client of all time, because this would have been unimaginable without you. Thanks too to Matilda Forbes-Watson – the real power behind the throne.

Huge thanks to Fenella Bates, Fi Crosby, Lindsey Evans and everyone at Penguin who worked on this book. And to Paula Castro for her gorgeous illustrations.

I wrote most of this book at Electric House and would like to thank Tom, Monica and all the wonderful staff there for sustaining me on illicit cake and lemon water. They take such good care of me that if I end up grand and impossible, it will be partly their fault.

Comfort & Hope

Cheers and Laughter

Book 2

By
Beverly Gooden-Wilson

British Library Cataloguing in Publication Data.
A catalogue record for this book is available from the British Library

ISBN 978 0 86071 734 8

A Commissioned Publication Printed by

MOORLEYS
Print, Design & Publishing
info@moorleys.co.uk · www.moorleys.co.uk

Introduction

Dear Reader,
I would like to take the opportunity of introducing you
to the second edition of the series 'Comfort and Hope'.
These two words have been on my lips
ever since I was handed a book written by a dear family friend
and sister in the Lord: Christine Mitchell.
From the day that Adam and Eve fell from grace
through their disobedience to the command of their Creator,
mankind has been in need of 'COMFORT AND HOPE'
and at times when the devil has made an attempt to depress me
and to wipe the smile from my face,
The Lord would send a timely word of consolation and restore my
soul, and that is what I am attempting to do in this booklet.
I do hope that you will enjoy these poems
and that somewhere in these pages you will find a poem that will
bring you comfort and hope,
cheers and laughter, or just one big smile.

Happy Reading.

Beverly Gooden-Wilson

Acknowledgment

Once again I would like to say a very big thank you to my
Heavenly Father for instructing me to write.
And what an awesome journey it has been as I read,
pray and meditate His Word.

But I also must say thanks to my assistants Joanne Lecky
and Wayne Thompson for the typing and graphics,
proof reading and their PATIENCE.
Truly they are an answer to prayer.

Thank you very much and may God continue to bless your lives
as you serve and honour Him in service for His glory.

Beverly

Comments Page

To me, Comfort & Hope is such a lovely series;
It is encouraging for people of all walks of life.
It is also a huge blessing to be a part of the
construction and design of these wonderful booklets!
(Wayne Thompson/IT Worker)

Within the pages of this book are some very thought-
provoking, imaginative, humorous and heart-warming
poems. Even while typing the poems they took me on
journeys down memory lane; triggered a song; made me
hopeful; encouraged and comforted me; even confirmed
some of my own thoughts and sometimes had me in fits of
laughter. The book certainly lives up to its title:
"Comfort & Hope, Cheers and Laughter" and I feel sure
that as you read them, you too will find a poem, or poems,
that you can identify with.
Enjoy!

(Joanne Lecky/PA Retired Civil Servant, Typist)

v

Contents

Title	Page No.
All For You	1
Have a Go If You Must	2
Sweet Words of Comfort and Hope	3
Respite	4
Sweetest Mother Of All	5
Woman of God (70)	6
Seventy Miraculous Years	8
My Heartfelt Thanks	10
Just Like King Solomon	11
The Sweetness Of Life	13
Sharing the Pain in Silence	14
You Can Make It	15
Mara the Cat	16
My Name is Dog	17
A Birthday Poem for Joanne Lecky	18
Playing Football and Scoring Goals	20
Summer Days	21
My Life	22
Notes	24

All For You

My brain must keep on thinking of you, who gave me life.

My ears must be keen to listen; when you speak I must be sure.

My eyes must keep on looking into your Holy Book.

My hands with these ten fingers must do the work they should.

My heart must keep on beating to keep me well and alive.

My feet must keep on moving, in perfect humble stride.

My knees must keep on bending as I choose to pray.

My mouth by which I'm nourished must feed upon your Word.

My teeth which chew each morsel must work to keep me strong.

My tongue and lips must join in the worship of you, my God.

Lord thank you for my body, what a joy it is to know,
That I can live and function freely from my head down to my toe!

Dear Lord, it gives me pleasure to live from day to day,
A wholly and anointed life in this lump of clay.

Refs: Ps 19:12-14, Prov 15:1-4,
Acts 13:18-25, Rom 9:18-21, St Matt 5:1-9

Have a Go If You Must

If the urge has come to you, then you know what you must do;
Go ahead, begin your quest, do some writing if you must.
If you do not have a plan, do not give up, you've just begun.
Let the inspiration flow, do your best, just have a go!
Whether morning, noon or night, you will get the urge to write!
Pen and paper, store them up, then begin, you'll never stop!
If at all you've past the test, you'll begin to woo your guests;
Who will say: "Write one for me!"
And you will say: "Just wait and see!"

You will join the writer's band, If you keep a pen in hand;
Poems and prose will come to mind, this will help you to unwind.
As you begin to do your stuff, your friends will never have enough!
Whether morning, noon or night, you will get the urge to write.
Then in time you will begin, take the paper and a pen;
To compose words of delight, all because 'one has to write'!
Your words will be clear and sound,
your thoughts wise, deep and profound;
If you've had these thoughts before,
Don't put it off, not any more.

Refs: Job 19:23, Hab 2:2

Sweet Words of Comfort and Hope

Speak to me: words that are sweet to my taste;
Speak to me words of *'Comfort and Hope'*;
The good and precious word of consolation
That will enhance and uplift my spirit.

Not words of falsehood, but of *truth*;
Not of bitterness, but of *love and meekness;*
Sweet and calm; pure and wholesome!

Speak to me; speak, so that the power of your words will revive me,
And will cause me to respond to the sweetness that is uttered.
I need to escape this spiritual drought,
That is causing me to be hungry, thirsty, anxious and hopeless!

Your input, your words of power spoken from your spirit to mine,
Will touch my soul, heal and revive me.
I am in desperate need of your help;
And how can anyone seek to offer comfort and hope,
To one who is as wounded in mind and spirit as I am right now,
With such **vain**... **cold**... and **empty**... words?!

Refs: 2 Cor 1:3-7, Job 21:22-34, Ps 119:49-56,
Ps 119:97-104, Num 22:31-35, Phil 4:1-9, Isa 59:4

R - e - s - p - i - t - e

T	=	Take a break: for goodness sake!
R	=	Rest for a while: then you can smile.
I	=	Inner peace: what calm release.
P	=	Pray in your heart: before you depart.
T	=	Today is the day so get on your way.
O	=	Over the hills and far away.
R	=	Relaxation and calm: works – like – a – charm!
E	=	Eat well, exercise, note the changes: surprise, surprise!
S	=	Sleep when you can: that's part of the plan.
P	=	Prolong your days: enjoy the new phase!
I	=	Improvement will come: maybe not for some.
T	=	Treasure these times: you've committed no crimes!
E	=	Enjoy the new you; that is what you should do: when at last, you are energized!!

Refs: St Mark 6:31, Is 30:15, Is 40:28-31, Matt 11:28-30

Sweetest Mother Of All
(Happy 70th Birthday)

God has given a gem to me, the sweetest mother of all;

Strong, confident, bold and wise, someone who loves to give all.

Forever listening when I call, ready to lift me when I fall,

Patient, loving, kind and true;

There's no other mother as sweet as you.

Carried me for 9 months in your womb,

After that you gave me a comfortable room.

Hugged me and fed me, day after day,

Taught me to live, and also to pray.

Never too busy to help me out,

Keen to assist, without a doubt.

What can I say Sweet Mother of mine?

You are a treasure, and a gift that's divine

Woman of God
(Happy 70th Birthday)

Woman of God, so Blessed; so dear,
The one to whom the Lord said: *"Write!"*
Many years ago she got the command,
She started to write then and still writes now!

From thought to pen, then pen to paper;
Words of wisdom, words of knowledge;
Words of encouragement, appreciation and love!
The Lord has Blessed her with this gift,
And from this command she cannot shift.

Who is this woman of whom I speak?
She's a 'Wife', a 'Mother' and 'Grandma' too.
To some she's 'Pastor', 'Sister', 'Friend',
To me she is dear Sister Bev,
But first and foremost, she's a child of God.

Woman of God, you are truly Blessed;
You have now reached '*THREE SCORE AND TEN*'!

Happy 70th Birthday, dear Sister Bev!

By Joanne Lecky

Pictures from the 70th Birthday
Poetry reading session

This is how I Celebrated my Birthday

Seventy Miraculous Years

Seventy years of miracles, seventy years old today.
Seventy years of Blessings, God is so good to me!
Seventy years providing, so that your eyes are blessed to see,
How He has formed and groomed me, into the image you now see.

He allowed this rare conception, within my Mother's womb;
Though young at heart and innocent, He safely brought her
through.
Then surely nine months later, a baby girl was born;
My Mother's little miracle, as nature took its course!

Seventy years of miracles, amidst the ups and downs;
The child she called 'A Dolly', grew into teenage years!
And then the good Lord spoke, and moved on my behalf;
By taking me to a foreign land, as these miracles unfold!

Seventy years of miracles, as I face the world at large;
And though somewhat unprepared, I was now living on my own.
With my childhood years behind me, new challenges daunt my path;
As I placed my faith in Jesus so the miracle unfolds.

Continued.....

Seventy years of miracles, signs and wonders in my life;
Such as my timely marriage, during my missionary years!
Then there was the dreadful stillbirth, of our very first child;
And my near-death experience, which followed just over one year!

Seventy years of coping, by the grace of God alone;
A life of signs and wonders, with so much to be thankful for!
Husband, children and grandchildren; a Mother who is still with us;
A team of Godly people, and (*the time to sit and write*)!!

Seventy years of labouring, of learning right from wrong;
With many joys and pleasures, tears and sleepless nights!
And when my life is ended and it is time to leave this world;
That will be (*THE GREATEST MIRACLE of My Entire LIFE*.)!!

Refs: Ps 90:4-10, Heb 1:10-12, Ps 77:10-15,
Hab 3:17-19, Ps 104:33-35

My Heartfelt Thanks

Loving Lord, I am so very grateful for the good times; the not so good and the not so great times; the happy days and the unhappy days; the glorious and the not so glorious years and memories. Loving Lord, I am determined to give thanks and praise to you always and to show my gratitude as long as I am alive.

Holy Spirit, fill my heart and soul with endless praise and gratitude; as I keep my eyes all fixed on you; giving thanks and praise in whatever I say and do: heartfelt praise and gratitude for the good times and the not… so… good times; the great times and the not… so… great times; the happy days and the unhappy days and in all the ups and downs that you have brought me through – safely through!

Thank you heavenly Father! I will give you what is due. Heartfelt thanks and praise to you; heartfelt thanks and praise. Amen!

Refs: St John 11:38-44, Ps 111:1-10, Ps 98:1-9, Ps 107:1-43

Just Like King Solomon

Dear Lord,
I know the kind of blessing that I need in my life,
I may not be like the great king Solomon of old;
But if you have been listening to any of my prayers,
Then you will know how to bless me, for this I am sure.

Please Lord, do a king Solomon's blessing on me,
Give me the wealth <u>and</u> the riches that is worthy of me;
Such as health and vigour to enjoy my new lifestyle,
And when I get my riches I will gladly pay my tithes.

Please God, do a king Solomon's blessing on me,
Acres of land and great mansions please.
Motorcars, aeroplanes, and sailing crafts; the lot!
Any kind of transport that moves like the wind;
To take me wherever I desire to go!

Continued…..

Please give me a king Solomon's blessing I pray,
I can't wait to be as rich and as famous as he was.
Bless me with knowledge to buy and to sell,
To do the stock market and not lose one cent;
Bless me with physical attraction and charm,
Vast earthly treasures, Lord fill up my barn!
Do a king Solomon's blessing on me,
And I will be faithful to the end;
Grant me Divine favour to live in this world.

If my words are presumptuous, forgive me O God;
But I would like to walk in king Solomon's shoes.
And as king Solomon was provided for,
Help me to succeed in all that I do
I would like to say thank you for hearing my prayers,
I am patiently waiting for your reply.
I hope you will answer before very long,
You've done it before Lord, please do it again.

The Sweetness Of Life

What type of fruit do you think you are?
A delicious mango? An apple or a pear? A fresh juicy orange? A ripe banana or a kiwi? A large water melon? Strawberry, raspberry, prune or grape? And are you aware of the treasure that's within: eternal life, hope, joy, love and peace? That's so if you are a Christian, sweetness and light is embedded in your soul. Just like the sweetness that is in your favourite fruit.

This reminds me of all the virtues, such as faith and love, goodness and mercy, compassion, strength and courage. These are all the precious seeds that's been invested in you and I, placed within by the might and wisdom of our Father God.

What is your favourite fruit that you just cannot have too much of?
One that is filled with sweetness and life: all the natural goodness that the body needs. Just like the Holy Spirit you can make someone's life brighter, richer and better as you radiate the sweetness and the glory that flows from the life of our loving Lord and Saviour Jesus Christ.

Refs: Ps 119:97-104, Gal 5:22-26,
Phil 4:1-9, Dan 12:1-3, James 3:13-18

 Sharing The Pain in Silence

My dear friends, throughout the years that we have known each other,
we have walked, talked, worked, prayed and laughed together;
as we enjoy the time and pleasures that true friendship allows.
On these numerous occasions we have shared our grievances
as we try to comprehend why some folks such as you and I
seem to suffer so much grief, and why it is that our trials
always seem to be greater than we can bear.
But you have often said: "Let us be still and wait on God;
our time of sorrow will one day be changed to great joy and gladness,
and the time will come when we all will be rejoicing together once more.
Our smile and laughter, joy and gladness will be coming from deep
within our spirits; for that which was meant for evil
shall work for our good! You mark my words.
But it is a comfort to know that you are always there for me and family."
Those were your words my friends. And you've also said: "Do not try to
offer many words of consolation that is meant to:
'CHEER ME UP' at this moment in time...
for right now those special words may be entirely useless to my grieving
heart and mind." We've heard that: "Silence is golden, it speaks louder
than words". That is so true isn't it? Nevertheless, let me say this:
"I appreciate you for being patient and understanding at this sad time."
Yes my dear friends, I shall try my very best to maintain the right balance
and keep the quality of silence that is required, as I allow you the time to
mourn the loss of your NEAREST AND DEAREST. I fully understand and
feel your pain, I am sharing the grief, I am so sorry for your loss.
Whether it be morning, noon or night, wherever I am I will be praying for
you and your family.

Rev 21:4

You Can Make It

Go on; go on, you can make it!
Go on my child, you can take it.
The journey seems long,
The mountain seems high!
But I am with you every step of the way.
Go on! I'll never leave you, go on my child;
I'll never forsake you.
The river is rough but trust in me,
Step by step I'll lead the way.
Go on; you can cross this valley.
Go on have faith in me. Do not listen to the enemy.
Do not fear you will never be ashamed.
Go on, go on! You can make it, of course you can;
soon you shall be in the Promised Land.
You can make it; you can make it!
Just walk by faith and not by sight
and you will get to your destination.
Come on; come on we can make it,
you are not alone do not be afraid!
We can cross this valley, we can climb this mountain,
we can cross that river and the red sea....!
"All things are possible if you believe in me."

Refs: Isa 30:15-21, St John 5:1-14,
Ps 23:1-6, St Matt 9:1-9, Phil 3:7-14

Mara the Cat

To you I may look like a grumpy old cat,
I do have a name but forget about that.
I've been around for a very long time,
When I was christened I hung my head in shame.
Lots of names were tested on me,
But I had no choice on which it would be.
Why should I live with a name like Mattie?
Give me a chance, O please, not Katie!

I was old and grumpy when I came to this house,
My owner had passed on and we were very close;
And amidst my grief I was without sympathy.
Why give me names that mean nothing to me?
I am a cat, C-A-T; can't you see?
What's your name then? You should have a name.
Yes, call me Mara, for that is the case;
Mara means bitter, this is a new phase.

My name is Cat, but Mara sounds great!
But these are some of the names that I hate;
Do not call me Molly or Gurtie or Fran,
Fanny, Cutie, Lettie or Dawn;
Of course I am grateful and somewhat relieved,
I hope that my new name will not add to my grief.

Dog - is My Name
(lady dog)

My name is dog, that's who I am,
It matters not where I came from.
I know you've got a name picked out,
Some fancy name I have no doubt.

My name is dog, remember that;
I'm not a parrot or a pussy cat.
I do not need any fancy names,
Just some dog food, some fun and games.

My name is dog, that's all, just dog;
I love and I'm so proud to be a dog.
And though I am a gorgeous female pet,
Please do not call me Paulette!

I am a dog; I am not like you,
Don't call me Tracy, Mitsy or Mo.
Don't call me Lilly and don't call me Nell,
Just call me dog and all will be well!

Don't call me Pixie or Queenie or Kate,
I am a dog and these names I hate.
I am a dog with four legs, not two,
I am a dog; I'm not like you.

A Birthday Poem
for Joanne Lecky

She may have retired from her usual post;
But Mrs. Joanne Lecky has no time to waste.
No job is too great and no job is too small,
If you need a helping hand, just give her a call.

Taking time out to care for the sick,
Hoping for better things week after week;
Holding back tears, yet weeping inside,
Trusting that God will comfort and guide.

Bearing the pain of losing her spouse;
Missing his presence when in the house
Sharing the joys of family life;
Fond memories of a devoted wife.

Continued.....

Fully committed to follow the Lord;
To walk in his footsteps and obey his word
She may have retired in the secular realm
But her work won't be finished until she is in heaven.

She may have retired from her nine to five role;
But she still labours on with heart and soul.
What will she be doing at eighty years old?
I believe that Joanne will be going for gold.

Joyfully doing her all-round jobs,
At home, in the office, she just never stops.
Typing up manuscripts, composing hymns;
Thank you Joanne Lecky for all of these things!

Prov 31:10-12, Luke 1:28

Playing Football
and Scoring Goals
(A Birthday Poem for Femi Sontan)

Playing football is my greatest pleasure.
When I score a goal it gives me great joy.
When I am on the pitch before the game begins,
I whisper a word of prayer to my father in heaven.
Wondering what my favourite sport is?
Playing football games, and scoring goals!

Playing this game is what I'm good at.
I'll play for money or just for love.
Playing football games, scoring lots of goals;
Giving God the glory as I chase the ball about.
Tackling, dribbling and scoring is great,
Saving, defending, and supporting the team.

Playing football games, scoring goals,
While praising the Lord with heart and soul.
Here comes the ball, let's have a go.
Here we go..... Praise the Lord, here we go!
My sympathy goes to the opposite side;
But Lord, give the victory to this team of mine.

When kicking the ball, I say, "Devil, get lost!"
Tired and weary, I take time to rest!
Whenever the team is feeling depressed,
I say, "Let us pray and ask God to bless."
Playing football, winning the game;
Giving honour to God and praising His name.

Summer Days

In the middle of the summer when the sun sends out its rays,
I forget about the winter with its cold and frosty days.
When it gets to wet October, then my heart begins to race.
But I soon recall with pleasure; long and happy summer days.

Summer days, O my days! Beaming, glorious, heavenly rays,
Warmer nights, with longer days;
Garden parties, morning prayers;
Time to stroll along the streams, time for lots of outdoor games,
Time to lounge beside the pool,
with mother nature, calm and cool.

Going back home, cooling off,
enjoying the weather, having a laugh;
Summer days, summer days, good old summer days!
Happy, glorious summer days;
I remember those summer days.

Why sit around and sing the blues;
Why lose my cool and blow a fuse?
I'll go to bed early, rise up with the dawn.
Put on my sunglasses and bask in the sun!

Summer days, summer days, warm and happy summer days!

 # *My Life*

My life is breathing in God's fresh air; working, playing, loving, giving, teaching, listening, caring, empathising, forgiving, encouraging, understanding.

My life is relaxation, rest, calm, quietness and enjoying the peace and tranquillity of a safe and healthy environment.

My life is going to bed, having a good night's rest, waking up to a brand new day, giving thanks to God for everything and having a healthy breakfast before getting into my daily routine.

My life is having a family to love and care for, who will not desert me when the going gets rough.

My life is knowing God; who He is and having His presence with me at all times.

My life is having lots and lots of fun and games with my children, grandchildren, nieces and nephews.

My life is having the love of my life – my beloved spouse – with me as much as possible; also having fun and laughter with family and friends.

My life is sharing, giving, reaching out and empathising whenever it is necessary for the good of others.

Continued.....

My life is being in a job that suits my personality, where I am paid the appropriate wage and where I am appreciated for my time, effort and skills.

My life is being a conscientious employee but enjoy rest and relaxation so as to avoid being over-stressed or having the 'Burnt Out Syndrome'. This will make me more committed and fulfilled.

My life is to teach, guide, protect and provide for those who are in my care; being a Parent, Guardian, Pastor, Helper, Carer, supporting them in their grief.

My life is to try my very best to be calm, composed and watchful in any disturbing situation and not to be distracted by any means.

My life is to forgive others as I need to be forgiven by them and more importantly by God.

My life is to encourage my peers who are feeling afraid and low in spirit to trust in God and be hopeful.

My life is to understand who I am; what is my destiny and how I can fulfil it, before I depart this world.

My life is to possess a contrite spirit, to show gratitude to my Creator for giving me, not only life, but 'Abundant Life' in Christ Jesus, His only Begotten Son, who is Lord and Saviour of the world.

This – is – My Life!!

Do you enjoy Poetry?

Would you like to take part in a Poetry Reading session with Bev & Co?

PLEASE CALL:

Beverly on 07905 470654

(email: Bevgood0277@gmail.com)

2017

January
S	M	T	W	Th	F	Sa
1	2	3	4	5	6	7
8	9	10	11	12	13	14
15	16	17	18	19	20	21
22	23	24	25	26	27	28
29	30	31				

February
S	M	T	W	Th	F	Sa
			1	2	3	4
5	6	7	8	9	10	11
12	13	14	15	16	17	18
19	20	21	22	23	24	25
26	27	28				

March
S	M	T	W	Th	F	Sa
			1	2	3	4
5	6	7	8	9	10	11
12	13	14	15	16	17	18
19	20	21	22	23	24	25
26	27	28	29	30	31	

April
S	M	T	W	Th	F	Sa
						1
2	3	4	5	6	7	8
9	10	11	12	13	14	15
16	17	18	19	20	21	22
23	24	25	26	27	28	29
30						

May
S	M	T	W	Th	F	Sa
	1	2	3	4	5	6
7	8	9	10	11	12	13
14	15	16	17	18	19	20
21	22	23	24	25	26	27
28	29	30	31			

June
S	M	T	W	Th	F	Sa
				1	2	3
4	5	6	7	8	9	10
11	12	13	14	15	16	17
18	19	20	21	22	23	24
25	26	27	28	29	30	

July
S	M	T	W	Th	F	Sa
						1
2	3	4	5	6	7	8
9	10	11	12	13	14	15
16	17	18	19	20	21	22
23	24	25	26	27	28	29
30	31					

August
S	M	T	W	Th	F	Sa
		1	2	3	4	5
6	7	8	9	10	11	12
13	14	15	16	17	18	19
20	21	22	23	24	25	26
27	28	29	30	31		

September
S	M	T	W	Th	F	Sa
					1	2
3	4	5	6	7	8	9
10	11	12	13	14	15	16
17	18	19	20	21	22	23
24	25	26	27	28	29	30

October
S	M	T	W	Th	F	Sa
1	2	3	4	5	6	7
8	9	10	11	12	13	14
15	16	17	18	19	20	21
22	23	24	25	26	27	28
29	30	31				

November
S	M	T	W	Th	F	Sa
			1	2	3	4
5	6	7	8	9	10	11
12	13	14	15	16	17	18
19	20	21	22	23	24	25
26	27	28	29	30		

December
S	M	T	W	Th	F	Sa
					1	2
3	4	5	6	7	8	9
10	11	12	13	14	15	16
17	18	19	20	21	22	23
24	25	26	27	28	29	30
31						

Notes